The
Dragonflies
of Hampshire

JOHN TAVERNER, STEVE CHAM, ALAN HOLD *et al.*

THE TEAM

EDITOR AND ORGANISER John Taverner

DATA RECORDERS Steve Cham, Peter Allen and Alan Hold

SPECIES MAPS AND HISTOGRAMS Steve Cham

BOOK COMMITTEE AND AUTHORS Peter and Cindy Allen, Steve Cham, Nicky Court, Chris Hall, Martin Harvey, Alan Hold, Derek Jenkins, Dan and Rosemary Powell, Tim Sykes, John Taverner, Chris and Bill Wain and David Winsland

ADVISERS AND HELPERS Steve Bailey, Linda Barker, David and Jean Dell, David Dimmock, Graham Vick

PHOTOGRAPHERS Cindy Allen, Peter Allen, Peter Burford, Steve Cham, Bob Gibbons, Martin Goodey, Barry Hilling, Alan Hold, Graham Sutton, John Taverner, Titchfield Haven rangers and Tony Welstead

SPECIES AND HABITAT SKETCHES Dan Powell

COVER PAINTING Rosemary Powell

MAPS OF HAMPSHIRE Figures 1 to 8 were produced by Hampshire Biodiversity Information Centre (HBIC, with special thanks to Nicky Court, Purgle Linham and Joanna Haigh), the Forestry Commission (with special thanks to Berry Stone) and the British Geological Survey (with special thanks to Simon Rippon). Figure 9 was produced by Steve Cham. All maps are of course based on Ordnance Survey material and we are pleased to include the Ordnance Survey in our list of acknowledgements.

Published by Pisces Publications

piscespublications

Funded by HBIC, the Hampshire County Council and a joint Hampshire and Isle of Wight Wildlife Trust/Environment Agency project grant.

Hampshire Biodiversity
Information Centre

Hampshire
County
Council

THE **wildlife** TRUSTS
**Hampshire &
Isle of Wight**

**ENVIRONMENT
AGENCY**

First published 2004 by Pisces Publications in association with the Hampshire County Council and the Environment Agency. Pisces Publications is the imprint of the **Nature**Bureau.

British Library-in-Publication Data.
A catalogue record for this book is available from the British Library.

ISBN 1-874357-26-9

Designed and produced by the **Nature**Bureau, 36 Kingfisher Court, Hambridge Road, Newbury, Berkshire RG14 5SJ.

Printed by Information Press, Oxford

CONTENTS

Part Five

Part Six

Part Seven

Appendix I

Appendix 2

INTRODUCTION

Around the close of the 20th century and the opening of the 21st, Hampshire has acquired a series of natural history books that set out for their various subjects the position of those species in the county at that time. These books are *The Flora of Hampshire* (Brewis, Bowman and Rose, 1996), *Birds of Hampshire* (Eyre and Clark, 1993), *The Butterflies of Hampshire* (Oates, Taverner and Green, 2000) and *The Moths of Hampshire and the Isle of Wight* (Goater and Norriss, 2001). A book on the dragonflies of the county would help to extend the written record of Hampshire's wildlife so that conservationists would be equipped with a considerable record of the status of many species, a record that can be used as a yardstick to judge how those species fare in years to come. This book covers vice-counties 11 and 12, but on species distribution maps the present administrative county boundary of Hampshire is shown and any records falling outside that line are from that part of vice-county 11 that used to be in Hampshire but is now in Dorset. We do this in order to be consistent with the county books on flora, butterflies and moths named above. The old county boundary is shown by a dotted line on the map of Solid Geology (Figure 1).

Hampshire is of national importance for its remaining areas of lowland heath. In addition, the New Forest is of both national and international importance for its range of habitat types and its rare flora and fauna. The area of southern England covered by Hampshire has the greatest variety of dragonflies anywhere in Great Britain (see national coincidence map on page 37).

To set out in detail the status of Hampshire's dragonflies and to report on the suitable habitat is the *raison d'etre* for this present volume. In the mid-20th century there was very little quantitative data available for Hampshire concerning its wildlife and without such data it was difficult for conservationists to judge the extent to which species were increasing or decreasing, or whether they were simply holding their own. Without accurate data, conservationists are denied their most valuable resource and they are less aware of those species that are coming under threat. Today, a massive amount of census work has transformed the situation so that we know the status of many species in considerable detail. If a decline in a species' numbers can be identified in the early stages, effective measures to halt or reverse that decline are much more likely to succeed than if measures are taken late in the day. We believe that this volume on the dragonflies of Hampshire will be of considerable interest to all those naturalists who are drawn to this fascinating order of insects, but the main value will probably be to conservationists.

ACKNOWLEDGEMENTS This volume is possible because a large number of dedicated field workers have spent countless hours in the field monitoring the distribution of dragonflies and to some extent trying to assess the strength of their populations. Between 1978 and the present day, which is the main period on which this volume concentrates, much of the county has been mapped and the records stored on a computerised database, although greater coverage is needed on the chalk where man-made pools have created a valuable habitat that has not really been studied in any detail. The names of all those who have contributed to this database are recorded in Appendix 1 at the end of the book and the Team who have brought all this together are listed on the title page.

We are also massively indebted to those who have funded the publication of this book. Books of this type are not produced for profit and they are made possible because there are donors who appreciate the need for such data to be available for conservationists. *The Dragonflies of Hampshire* exists because it is supported through a joint Hampshire and Isle of Wight Wildlife Trust/Environment Agency project grant and by an equal contribution from the Hampshire Biodiversity Information Centre (HBIC, under the wing of Hampshire County Council). Without them, there would be no book; it is as simple as that.

We also pay tribute to our publisher, Pisces Publications at Newbury, for all their work in producing this volume, with special thanks to Peter Creed for his contributions to layout. Maps have been produced by HBIC, the Forestry Commission, the British Geological Survey and Steve Cham, most of them tailor-made for this book, our thanks going to Nicky Court, Purgle Linham and Joanna Haigh (HBIC), Berry Stone (Forestry Commission) and Simon Rippon (British Geological Survey) respectively for their work, and of course to Ordnance Survey whose maps are the basis for those in this volume.

Amongst the many others who have contributed are Tim Woodfine and the Marwell Preservation Trust who have made available to us all the dragonfly records from Eelmoor Marsh SSSI, Carolyn Steele of the Dorset Environmental Records Centre who gave us access to records from those areas of Dorset that lie within vice-county 11 (South Hampshire), and Linda Barker who went through the text with a tooth comb to check for inconsistencies, errors and like points that can spoil a text. Mike Thurner took a mass of the earlier Hampshire records and processed them so that they were compatible with Steve Cham's database and then did the same for records along the Blackwater Valley. As a consequence of Mike's work, a mass of data was made readily available for the species' distribution maps that appear in this book.

The Team that I brought together includes respected odonatists who have studied their subject in Hampshire for a number of years. Together we planned the outlay of this volume and apportioned sections of the text for each individual to write. At the end of each year, the text was circulated to all the team for their comments and we would then meet to see how the text should be revised. Steve Cham is the National Dragonfly Recorder and apart from going through the text and suggesting changes, all the species distribution maps and histograms of flight times are his work. Alan Hold has constantly reviewed and modified the text. Chris Hall has been quite invaluable with his meticulous comments and advice concerning those parts of the text that deal with the Basingstoke Canal and its surrounding area; his knowledge of the Odonata in those places has transformed the text that deals with those parts. Peter and Cindy Allen wrote a section on past dragonfly studies in Hampshire, as well as providing excellent photographs of species. David Winsland wrote a fine piece on the New Forest, Nicky Court contributed a section on conservation, and all team members produced their own contributions either by writing some species accounts, such as Chris and Bill Wain, or by their detailed knowledge of specific points, such as Derek Jenkins' and his long-term study of the New Forest's Southern Damselflies. Rosemary and Dan Powell are two of Hampshire's leading wildlife artists; Rosemary produced the magnificent cover painting whilst Dan's attactive sketches decorate a few of the earlier pages. Consequently, the result is truly a team effort, regardless of whose names appear on the cover. Indeed, in the field of Odonata, I am one of the least experienced of The Team.

Finally, we are much indebted to Ordnance Survey and Mike Proctor, Liaison Officer with Hampshire County Council, who came to an agreement that as this is a non profit-making book with a serious conservation purpose, we could use Ordnance Survey-based material free of charge on the County Council licence.

In Part Four, which is the Systematic List of species, each dragonfly and damselfly is headed with the English and scientific names. Throughout the rest of the text, only the English name is used. English names are also used in the text where birds, flowers, butterflies or moths occasionally appear, and for the sake of county uniformity, these names are those used in the Hampshire books covering those fields that are mentioned in the opening paragraph of this Introduction. Scientific names of those species are listed in Appendix 2 at the end of this book.

In English, the word dragonfly can be ambiguous because it can be used either to cover the whole Order (Odonata), or simply to cover the Anisoptera (dragonflies) as opposed to the Zygoptera (damselflies). The Editor considers that it is fairly obvious when reading the text whether the word dragonfly is being used to cover the whole order or simply the Anisoptera.

John Taverner, March 2004

DEFINITIONS OF TECHNICAL TERMS

British (UK) Biodiversity Action Plan, (BAP) This was produced in 1994 by the Government to demonstrate its commitment to the Convention on Biological Diversity which it signed up to in Rio de Janeiro in 1992. The Plan sets out the framework for a series of priority species and habitat action plans which were then produced by the UK Biodiversity group between 1995 and 1999 (Volumes II–V). The UK Plan also contains guidance for preparing local biodiversity action plans.

County Rare A species recorded in eleven or fewer tetrads.

County Scarce A species recorded in 12–42 tetrads.

Diapause This is a mechanism whereby dragonfly larvae are able to accommodate adverse climatic conditions by entering a state of suspended development. A combination of both reduced daylight hours and a lowering of water temperature in the autumn trigger the onset of diapause and the resumption of development is triggered by the reverse in spring. In some species this occurs in the ova, but in most it takes place in the larval stages.

Emergence The term used for larvae coming out of water to hatch.

European Habitats Directive The actual title is the *European Community Council Directive (92/43) on the Conservation of Natural Habitats and Wild Flora and Fauna.* It requires Member States to take measures to maintain or restore natural habitats and wild species at a favourable conservation status in the Community. Annex II of the Directive lists animals and plants of Community interest whose conservation requires the designation of Special Areas of Conservation (SACs). The Southern Damselfly is the only UK species of Odonata on Annex II (apart from the Orange-spotted Emerald which is now extinct in Britain).

Eutrophic Water that is rich in dissolved nutrients, often with nitrates and phosphates from agricultural fertilizers, but often shallow and seasonally deficient in oxygen.

Exuvia An empty larval case from which a dragonfly has hatched (pl. exiviae).

Hampshire Biodiversity Action Plan, H(BAP) This was produced in 1998 by a partnership of organisations that have an influence on the conservation of biodiversity in Hampshire. The Hampshire BAP effectively translates the objectives set out in the UK BAP into action at a local level. A series of action plans have been prepared for those habitats and species listed in the UK BAP where they occur in Hampshire, plus other species which are of particular concern in Hampshire.

Key Sites Project This was an initiative set up jointly by the Biological Records Centre and the British Dragonfly Society in 1988 to gather breeding data and identify Key Sites for nationally rare and threatened species.

Mesotrophic Water where the dissolved nutrients are moderate in quantity (see Eutrophic and Oligotrophic).

Oligotrophic Water that has few dissolved nutrients, with low levels of calcium, nitrates, phosphates, and similar nutrients. Such waters are usually acidic.

Outstanding Assemblage of Species or **Outstanding Assemblage Sites (OAS)** Sites that have a large assemblage of dragonflies are given this title. The number of species concerned depends on the part of Britain in which the site is situated, a good site in northern Scotland having fewer than a good site in a county such as Hampshire. As Hampshire is recognised as having a large number of species, an OAS is regarded as a site where more than 18 species are breeding or are likely to be found. A list of such sites is given in Part Five.

Nationally Scarce Species in this category usually occur in 16 to 100 ten-kilometre squares in Britain, although a species that is considered to be especially threatened may be included if it occurs in more than 100 square kilomertres.

Oviposition The act of egg laying.

Population Densities are difficult to describe with any comparative meaning between different species and types of dragonfly. This is because of the widely differing needs and habitat requirements brought about primarily by the different sizes of both genera and species. Whereas a particular habitat may harbour a maximum population of 500 damselflies at any one time, similar maximum populations of darter and hawker species may well be in the region of 20 and 5 respectively. Because of this, numerical comparisons between differing types can be somewhat misleading. It is worth remembering that bank length is usually more significant than water area, except in the case where aquatic vegetation can provide additional 'edge' habitat.

Red Data Book Species These are severely threatened species, most of which occur in 15 or fewer ten-kilometre squares in Britain, but the inclusion of a species in this category is also based on threat and not just rarity so that some species occurring in more than 15 ten-kilometre squares may be in the Red data Book category. RDB Category 1, Endangered. RDB Category 2, Vulnerable. RDB Category 3, Rare.

Secondary rocks Rocks that were laid down between the Primary rocks and the Tertiaries. They are of the Triassic, Jurassic and Cretacious ages.

Species Action Plan, (SAP) These have several objectives – to provide information, establish targets for action, direct conservation work, raise awareness and provide a monitoring framework. Both the UK and Hampshire SAPs contain information on status, distribution, designations, habitat requirements, factors affecting the species, current actions and proposed actions with lead agencies identified. The Southern Damselfly is the only priority Odonata species for which a SAP has been written in both the UK and Hampshire BAPs.

Spring species These spend the last winter before emergence as the final larval instar and consequently typically emerge synchronously and early (Corbet, 1954).

Summer species These spend the last winter before emergence before the final larval instar and consequently typically emerge later and with less synchronisation than spring species (Corbet, 1954).

Tandem When mating, the male grasps the female by the back of her head and the pair so joined together are said to be 'in tandem'.

Teneral This is used to describe the period of time when the newly emerged dragonfly is most vulnerable to predators. Immediately after emergence, the cuticle and the wings are insufficiently hardened to enable the insect to fly in a sustained manner and in this state the insect is termed teneral. The length of time that the dragonfly is in this state is quite variable but in warm, dry weather it is seldom more than an hour. After the insect has completed its initial flight it is known as a *sub-adult* when the wings are not fully hardened and the adult body colours have not yet developed.

Tertiary rocks Those that follow Secondary rocks in geological time. Upper, Middle and Lower Chalk were the last of the Secondary rocks to be laid down in Hampshire. London Clay, the Reading Beds and the younger sands and gravels that make up the New Forest and most of north Hampshire are all Tertiary rocks, laid down between 65 and 1.8 million years ago (see Figure 1).

Wildlife Countryside Act, 1981, Schedule 5 This Act, and later amendments, lists certain species of animal (other than birds) which may be protected from intentional killing, injury or taking; intentional or reckless damage, destruction or obstruction to a place of shelter or protection; selling, possessing or transporting for purpose of sale. Not all the species listed in Schedule 5 receive protection from all the acts just mentioned. There are 100 species listed, plus all bats, turtles and cetaceans. Two Odonata species are listed, these being the Southern Damselfly and the Norfolk Hawker.

PART ONE

GEOLOGY AND HYDROLOGY OF HAMPSHIRE

SOLID GEOLOGY The solid geology of Hampshire is relatively simple. Much of the county is occupied by a central mass of Upper, Middle and Lower Chalk, the vast majority of this being the softer Upper Chalk. This is bounded to both north and south by younger rocks, these being bands of London Clay and sandy Reading Beds, and then more extensive areas of Tertiary rocks that are a mixture of sands, gravels and clays. In north Hampshire, the London Clay forms a more extensive belt than it does in the south. In eastern Hampshire, the western extremity of the eroded Wealden anticline occupies a small part of the county, the rocks being Upper Greensand, Gault Clay and Lower Greensand. There are minor exceptions to this general pattern, such as the Chalk fold that breaks through the younger rocks in the south to form the Portsdown Hills, but from the point of view of dragonfly habitat, the pattern described here and in the accompanying Geological Map are sufficient to appreciate the distribution maps for each species (see Figure 1).

Figure 1. The solid geology of Hampshire
Map produced by the British Geological Survey with especial thanks to Simon Rippon

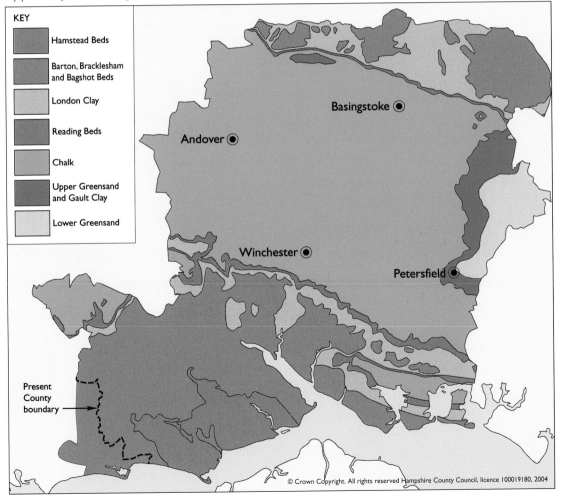

KEY

- Hamstead Beds
- Barton, Bracklesham and Bagshot Beds
- London Clay
- Reading Beds
- Chalk
- Upper Greensand and Gault Clay
- Lower Greensand

Basingstoke ●

Andover ●

Winchester ●

Petersfield ●

Present County boundary

The central mass of Chalk forms rolling hill country that is largely given over to cereal farmland, with wheat and barley being the main crops. These create prairie-like expanses where chemicals and lack of wild flowers keep many forms of wildlife at bay. In recent years, farm subsidies and agricultural diversification have seen crops such as oilseed rape and flax becoming commonplace. Unfarmed Chalk downland exists as scattered patches, mostly small and well separated from their nearest neighbouring downland patch, but there is a considerable cover of both deciduous and coniferous woodland, although much of this cover exists mainly as small or medium-sized woods.

Much of this vast area is devoid of natural water as the rock is so porous. Main rivers such as the Avon, Test, Itchen and Meon have cut through the Chalk mass so that their water-tables are above the surface. Apart from these and a number of winterbournes, water on the Chalk occurs only in man-made pools such as ornamental garden ponds and the occasional dew-pond, or where there is a cover of clay-with-flints, although the last-named does not give rise to water in any quantity.

Consequently, the chalklands are not naturally suitable breeding habitat for insects that require surface water as an essential element in their life style, although it will be shown in a later section that the sum total of man-made ponds forms a considerable and valuable habitat. Following emergence, individuals disperse away from water to avoid the intense competition of other males at the breeding site. It is during this maturation phase that individuals often appear on the dry chalk, and many of the dispersive species will wander far and wide in search of new sites, sometimes recorded as they move through the chalklands. Adult females may occur on the chalk when they have moved away from breeding waters between matings, or males in dull weather when they too have moved away from water to hunt.

The main river valleys and rocks other than Chalk form the most important natural dragonfly habitats in the county. The Tertiary rocks in the north of Hampshire have seen a great deal of their natural habitat disappear due to the growth of housing, forestry, industry, roads and like development, as well as neglect, but in the south those same Tertiaries in the

Figure 2. Heathland and mires of the New Forest

Map produced by the Forestry Commission with special thanks to Berry Stone.

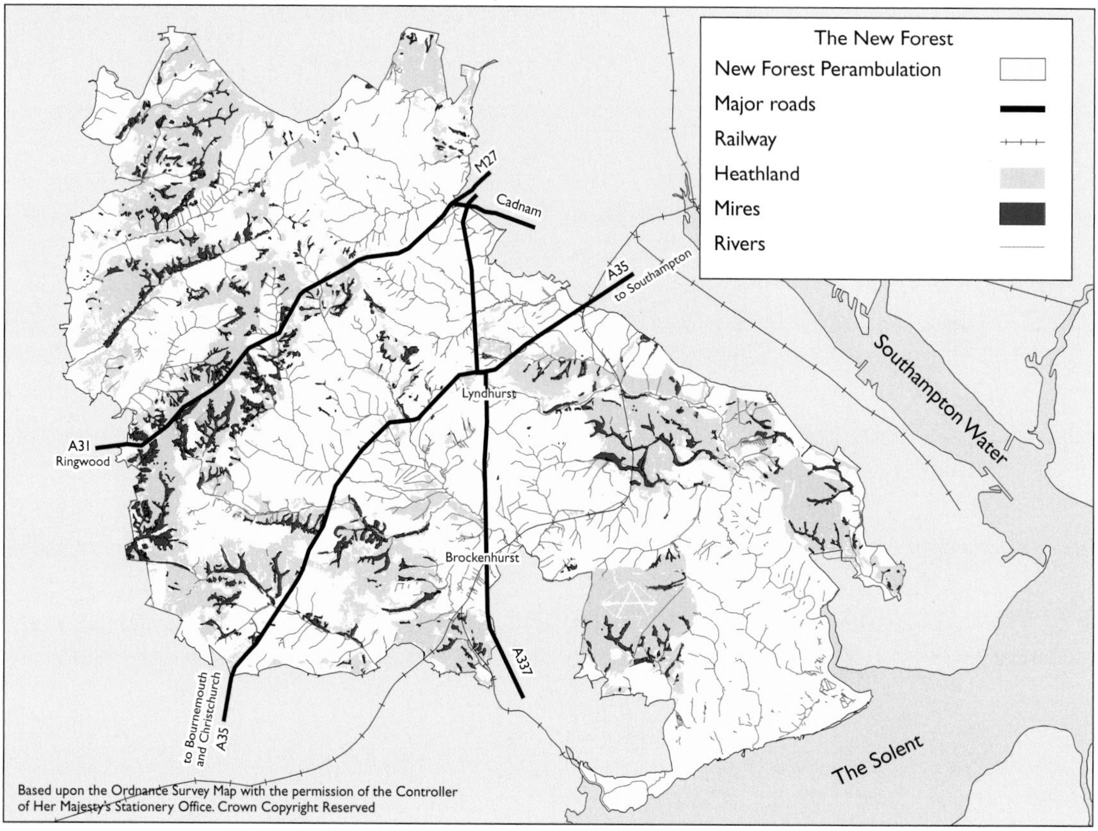

New Forest have been saved from such a fate by the Forest's history and ownership. Here, the impervious nature of the Bagshot, Bracklesham, Barton and Hamstead Beds result in much surface water with many small, natural ponds, a number of large man-made lakes and many mires and bogs, whilst the relief of the land is such that streams are mostly small and slow-flowing. This places the Tertiary rocks of the New Forest and parts of its surrounding fringe amongst the finest dragonfly habitats in Britain (see Figures 2 and 3). Indeed, it takes only a quick glance at the species' distribution maps in Part Four to show that the Tertiary rocks of both north and south Hampshire hold the core of our dragonfly populations.

Most New Forest ponds hold important dragonfly populations, but the ones listed below have consistently produced a pleasing range of species in reasonably good numbers. Some have deteriorated in recent years; these are marked with an asterisk and the list is followed by a brief paragraph that suggests reasons for such declines.

Sheepwash Pond, East End	SZ 364976 *	East End Gravel Pit, East End	SZ 366976
Sowley Pond	SZ 3796	Blackwater complex, Needs Ore	SZ 4197
Linbrook Lake	SU 159072	Long Pond South	SU 198019 *
Long Pond North	SU 199022	Whitten Pond	SU 204013
Slufters Pond complex	SU 222096	Mogshade Pond, Highland Water	SU 242096
Broomy Pond	SU 212107 *	Eyeworth Pond (Irons Well)	SU 228146
Tucker's Bridge Pond	SU 341037	Rowbarrow Pond	SU 357045 *
Hatchet Pond complex	SU 3601	Furzey Pond	SU 386067
Stonyford Pond	SU 413040	Holbury Mill Pond	SU 424042
Ashley Walk pools and bomb craters	SU 2114		

Figure 3. Streams and ponds in the New Forest
Map produced by the Forestry Commission with special thanks to Berry Stone.

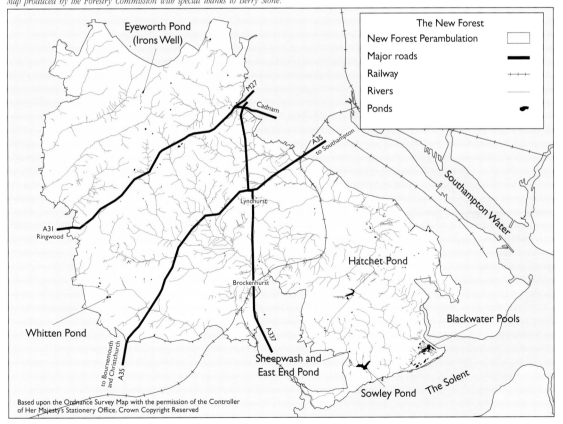

Based upon the Ordnance Survey Map with the permission of the Controller of Her Majesty's Stationery Office. Crown Copyright Reserved

Figure 4. Ponds, wet heaths, fens and mires in (a) northern Hampshire and (b) the Hampshire Weald

Maps produced by HBIC with special thanks to Purgle Linham and Nicky Court

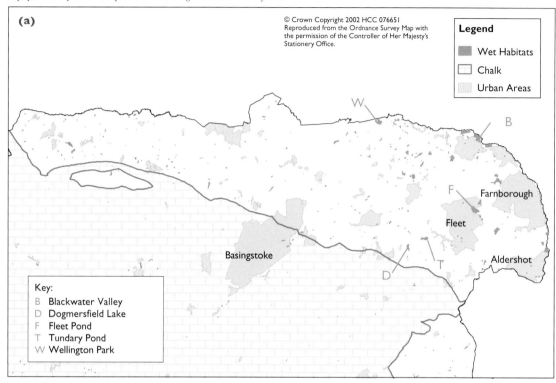

Sheepwash Pond has rapidly disappeared under aquatic vegetation and now has a very limited area of open water. Long Pond South has been prone to extensive drying in recent years. Broomy Pond deteriorated when a valve at the back of the pond was accidentally opened, whilst Rowbarrow Pond has deteriorated rapidly over the past few years, possibly as a result of scrub clearance to the west of the adjacent stream. If the New Forest ponds are to remain attractive to Odonata, some attention must be paid to their maintenance.

As for the London Clay, Reading Beds, Lower Greensand and Gault Clay, these rocks are far less porous than the Chalk and so they contain surface water. Their importance as suitable habitat for dragonflies is simply limited by the relatively small area that they cover, but the distribution maps under each species show that they are not unimportant. However, in the east of the county the small part of the Wealden anticline with Lower Greensands and heavy, impervious Gault Clay have a not inconsiderable area where surface water is commonplace, the result being that there are a number of sites that hold useful populations of Odonata.

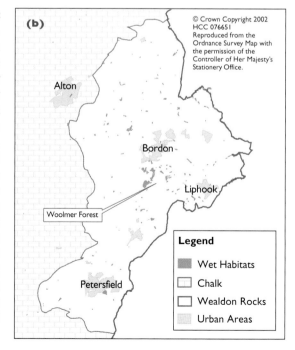

HYDROLOGY The basic drainage pattern over most of Hampshire is from north to south. The central Chalk is cut by the valleys of the Avon, Test, Itchen and Meon and due to the porosity of the rock, these rivers have few tributaries. Those that do exist are either very short or appear in the form of winterbournes. In the north of the county, streams on the Tertiary rocks drain into the catchment area of the Thames, whilst the water flowing off the eastern greensands and Gault Clay drain into the Rivers Arun and Wey, the latter river then flowing into the Thames.

Apart from these natural rivers, there is one man-made watercourse that is of considerable importance to dragonflies. This is the Basingstoke Canal that runs across the county for some 20 kilometres from Up Nately to Aldershot and has been covered by several excellent observers for a number of years. The route is depicted in Figure 6 (see page 24).

The above descriptions of the solid geology and the hydrology of Hampshire set the foundation for the following text and help to show why the county figures amongst the finest in England for this order of insects. Some of the main towns of Hampshire are shown on the maps so that readers can place localities more easily.

Figure 5. The main hydrology of Hampshire
Map produced by HBIC with special thanks to Purgle Linham and Nicky Court

Key:
A   Andover
Al Aldershot
B   Basingstoke
E   Eastleigh
F   Farnborough
Fl Fleet
G   Gosport
P   Petersfield
Po Portsmouth
R   Ringwood
S   Southampton
W   Winchester

© Crown Copyright 2002 HCC 076651
Reproduced from the Ordnance Survey
Map with the permission of the Controller
of Her Majesty's Stationery Office.

Legend
— Rivers
☐ Chalk
▨ Major Urban Areas

PART TWO

THE HUMAN INFLUENCE ON DRAGONFLIES

Because we have altered the natural habitat to such a dramatic extent, it was felt that this section should appear before Part Three where each habitat type is covered in detail. Over the past millennium, there can be no doubt that we have destroyed much suitable dragonfly habitat as we have adapted the natural countryside to suit our needs, but equally there is no doubt that we have also created habitat that is good or even ideal for this group of insects. On balance in Hampshire, it is debateable whether our influence has been positive or negative in this respect. In the world of butterflies this question is not in doubt in the county; it is patently clear that our influence on butterfly populations, mainly through habitat destruction, has been nothing short of disastrous, especially in the New Forest. However, there was never any widespread attempt to kill and preserve dragonflies in collections, as was the case with birds, butterflies and moths, mainly because it has proved almost impossible to preserve dragonflies well as their colours soon fade and eventually disappear. There have been various attempts to overcome this problem, as mounted specimens would be useful in places such as museums, but none has been wholly successful. Consequently, there was not the wholesale destruction of these insects by collectors as happened with butterflies, where in Victorian times the New Forest was a major centre for collectors and local lepidopterists made a living by selling specimens or acting as guides to visitors. Dragonfly collections appear today, but these are in the form of photographs where the insects are spared save for a brief intrusion on their privacy.

We will never be able to answer the question as to whether our development of the natural landscape has been beneficial or detrimental to dragonflies as a whole with any degree of certainty, because there is no quantitative data from the past to compare with the quite detailed information that we have now collected, especially in the last two or three decades. It may be possible, for some species with highly specialised needs, to show that our influence has not been beneficial, but the main aim in this section of the book is not to arrive at an overall conclusion one way or the other, but merely to identify those of our activities that have influenced dragonfly numbers and to give examples from all parts of the county.

Let us look on the bright side and take the positive features first, considering these under a number of sub-headings. Not many of these beneficial actions have been deliberately aimed at creating good wildlife habitat; any such gains have mostly been by chance when man has changed the landscape for his own advantage, but the reasons for change are not quite so important if the results are friendly to wildlife.

COASTAL DEFENCE WORK The stretches of wilder coast in Hampshire contain a number of waters that result from our attempts to guard the low-lying coast against marine invasion. Sea-walls have been built at a number of localities, such as those that stretch from Keyhaven to Lymington, from Park Shore to the mouth of the Beaulieu River, at the mouth of the River Hamble, Titchfield Haven, Farlington Marshes and on the southern shore of Hayling Island. These coastal defences not only keep the sea at bay but they act as dams on the landward side, preventing water from flowing to the sea. Consequently, fields have to be drained by a series of ditches leading to sluices, such as those that cross the fields at Needs Ore Point and Farlington Marshes, whilst water collects immediately behind the walls to create marshes and pools such as those found at Pennington, Titchfield Haven and Park Shore. These coastal habitats that are the results of man's sea defences cover a considerable area of land and being a congregation of wet meadows, ditches, marshes and pools of varying size, often with suitable growths of vegetation, they can contain very healthy populations of Odonata. They are, of course, an example of wildlife habitat being created by chance, as mentioned in the previous paragraph, but they have provided suitable habitat where previously there was just salt-marsh or shore that would have been wholly devoid of dragonflies.

LARGE AND SMALL MAN-MADE LAKES AND PONDS These have been created for a number of reasons in all areas of the county. Within the New Forest there are a number of important waters and further information is given in Part Three under the New Forest heading; the waters named here are merely examples and do not form a comprehensive list. Eyeworth Pond was made to provide water for an explosives factory that operated nearby around the turn of the 19th and 20th centuries; Sowley Pond was created to provide power for hammer mills, and Hatchet Pond was also modified for this purpose after its original creation which came from the digging of marls to spread on the infertile Forest soils; Blackwater, by the mouth of the Beaulieu River, may have been an ancient fish pond for the nearby monastery; East End gravel pit was created for watering livestock. All of these waters hold considerable populations of dragonflies and there is nothing to suggest that the natural New Forest had any area the size of these ponds that held such a concentration and variety of species. There are also smaller man-made ponds within the Forest boundary, such as the small but splendid pond dammed by the road that runs past Hatchet Pond towards Lymington, and whilst these do not compare with the large waters named in this paragraph, they nevertheless swell the stock of potential dragonfly habitat. All the large Forest pools are man-made, a curious point in view of the Forest's impervious nature. It has been suggested that Whitten Pond, near Burley, is an exception to this statement, but although there is a natural depression in the ground here that contained water, boards have been placed across the outlet stream that have held back the water and created the larger pool that we see today. All the natural pools are small, although there are considerable areas of natural bog. In view of this, it seems probable that the past history of the New Forest has seen our activities do much to improve the dragonfly habitat for most species rather than lead to a deterioration.

These excellent waters are not only creations of the past; they are still being built. Embley Wood lies some two kilometres outside of the New Forest perambulation, situated on the same Tertiaries that form the northern Forest, and in the distant past it was a part of the Embley Park estate, home of Florence Nightingale. In Florence Nightingale's time, the estate had several large man-made lakes that had become neglected by the mid 20th century. Brian and Jean Sutton, the present owners of part of the wood that contains one of these old lakes that is now called Sable Pond, have put in a tremendous amount of work to change what was a heavily overgrown area to quality wildlife habitat, with particular attention to the creation of areas suitable for dragonflies. Neglect of Sable Pond had led to the lake becoming completely overgrown by Rhododendrons, and Brian Sutton has cleared this water, which covers an area about the size of two and a half football pitches, until today it forms a prime dragonfly site. Around this pool, Brian has dug a network of smaller ponds and linking ditches and cleared masses of Rhododendron to allow heath to regenerate, so that the resulting combination of large pool, small ponds and the accompanying system of ditches, bog, heath and forest (together known as Sable Waters) provides a man-made dragonfly habitat that can be numbered not only amongst the best in the county but amongst the best in the country. Twenty-three species of dragonfly have been recorded there, in considerable numbers, and without the activities of man the whole area would be but a shadow of its present self as suitable habitat for these insects. Happily, much of the remaining area of Embley Wood is owned by Peter McMurray who has similar plans to develop his portion as an area that is attractive for wildlife, whilst yet another part of the old Florence Nightingale estate contains the man-made Kentford Lake where the present owner has created two smaller pools nearby that are very similar to some of the recent pools built by the Suttons in Embley Wood.

Another deliberate attempt to attract dragonflies has been the creation of Old Bursledon Nature Haven by John Horne. John moved to Old Bursledon in 1982 and having an interest in wildlife from his youth, dug five spring-fed ponds. In 1987 he purchased 65 acres around his house that included water meadows, marshes and an SSSI. In 1992 he had to sell 50 acres south of the railway to Hampshire County Council, but he placed covenants on the land to ensure it would remain a nature reserve to which he had access for study. By 2003, the number of ponds had increased from five to 39, deliberately planned so that they provided a variety of habitats to attract a mix of species; some were morning ponds and others were afternoon ponds, according to how surrounding vegetation shaded the water. Some were spring ponds, others autumn ponds, and so on. Apart from the digging of ponds, there has been much other work designed to make the land suitable for a range of wildlife, with the result that 17 species of dragonfly have been recorded breeding there and over 20 species have been seen. This is all in a subsoil of clay beside the Hamble River, much of the material being laid down by the Hamble over the ages. Such work by John Horne, along with that of the Suttons described in the previous paragraph, has had an enormously beneficial effect on dragonfly populations and we have to be thankful for the effort and expense that such dedicated conservationists have put into making their lands wildlife havens.

Away from the New Forest, but also in the southern Tertiaries, other pools have been created for a number of reasons, some of these being in Nature Reserves. One such pool is Toby's Pond in Botley Wood, which in many respects resembles Embley Wood. This is a Hampshire County Council Nature Reserve and the pond in question is set in an area that appears to be natural, wild woodland but which in fact is a carefully controlled habitat developed by Barry Duffin and his team of rangers. The place where Toby's Pond has been made was a damp depression that has been deepened and is now home to species such as Downy Emerald. Previously, it did not hold anything approaching the population or variety of dragonflies that it boasts today. Another site is Swanwick Nature Reserve, currently managed by the Hampshire and Isle of Wight Wildlife Trust, which contains a number of quite large pools that are also man-made, the hollows being the result of clay digging in the first decades of the 20th century to provide materials for a local brick industry. The pools hold a very healthy and varied population of dragonflies that also includes the locally distributed Downy Emerald.

The northern Tertiary rocks also have large man-made ponds, Shortheath, Kingsley, Bourley, Ancell's Farm, Warren Heath and Heath Warren Ponds being examples, and these are also excellent dragonfly habitats with a large range of species. Woolmer Pond and Longmoor ranges are also important sites in this area, as is the complex of old gravel pits in the Blackwater Valley (further details of the last-named gravel pits will appear below).

The reasons for man-made ponds, large and small, are many and varied, but gravel extraction has created a number of important waters once the gravel has been exhausted and the pits become flooded. There are such disused gravel pits in the Avon Valley between Ringwood and Fordingbridge, near Romsey at Casbrook Common and in the north of the county there is a complex of gravel pits around Yateley and the Blackwater Valley. Some of these disused gravel pits have become wonderful habitats for dragonflies. In the Blashford pits, alongside the Avon just above Ringwood, the variety of species and the numbers of some species are very impressive, and an important proportion of the area is run as a wildlife reserve by the Hampshire and Isle of Wight Wildlife Trust. At two of these Blashford gravel pits (Ivy Lake and Ellingham Lake), between 15.00hrs and 17.00hrs in bright, warm sunshine on 20th June 2003, many hundreds of Common Blue Damselflies were seen flying singly or in tandem over just a small portion of each lake, and it is probable that the population of this species on both lakes ran into thousands. In places the surface of the two lakes was shimmering with blue as sunlight caught the males; pairs in tandem were everywhere, and towards late afternoon, when the insects were closing down for the day, the lakeside vegetation looked as though it had bright blue flowers hanging from twigs and branches as the males prepared for the night, whilst the floating vegetation was also alive with the species. Alan Hold and John Taverner, who recorded the scene, found it a most impressive sight. Unfortunately, there has not been a comprehensive survey of dragonflies on these Avon gravel pits, and it must be a priority over the next few seasons to carry out such work.

The gravel pits along the Blackwater Valley, in north-eastern Hampshire, have been surveyed in greater detail and a splendid booklet, *Blackwater Valley Dragonflies* (Crick and Bennett, 2003) is available from the Blackwater Valley Countryside Partnership. The booklet names no fewer than 30 species of dragonfly and damselfly that have been recorded in recent years, and although a few of these are rather rare migrants or species that have put in casual appearances, the Blackwater gravel pits must rank amongst the most important sites in Hampshire, if not in Britain, although some of the waters are shared with neighbouring counties. Were it not for these man-made pits, the tally of species would certainly be fewer, with numbers of most species well below the levels that are reached today. Happily, the valley is a protected area and many of the sites have been restored with wildlife and controlled public access in mind. Apart from the booklet on dragonflies, the Blackwater Valley Countryside Partnership have also published a booklet (*Blackwater Valley Path* – Bailey, 2001) that is an excellent guide to visitors who wish to examine this superb area. The following paragraph is a précis of Steve Bailey's account of the valley waters.

The Blackwater Valley from Aldershot to Eversley holds around 80 waterbodies, about 50 of these being medium-sized lakes formed by old gravel diggings from the 1940s to the present. The other waters are mainly smaller ponds created by urban and roadside drainage schemes. Of the 80 waterbodies, around half lie in Hampshire, although frequent realignments of the River Blackwater have left the county boundary irrelevant in ecological terms. The odonate populations have been well studied and are controlled by age of the waterbody and fish stocks, many of the lakes being heavily stocked for angling. The heavily stocked fishing lakes obviously have a limited breeding success for dragonflies, but at moderately stocked angling lakes, 11 species of Odonata are recorded regularly as adults. Two species fare particularly well, even on the angling lakes, these being the Red-eyed Damselfly and the Common Blue Damselfly. On the smaller and newer ponds, and even on operational gravel pits, Emperors, Broad-bodied Chasers and Four-spotted Chasers are found and as the silt beds develop into shallow ponds and swamps, the Emerald Damselfly, Southern Hawker and Ruddy Darter begin to appear. Where trees develop around these sites, Brilliant Emeralds can occasionally be seen.

Put all the waters mentioned so far together and they go some way to making good the pools that we have drained over the years. Of those waters named so far, only Toby's Pond, the Sable Waters pools and Old Bursledon Nature Haven were deliberately created for wildlife, whilst Sable Pond – a part of the Sable Waters complex – and the Blackwater gravel pits were renovated especially with dragonflies in mind, but the damage we have done to wetlands was not with the intent of damaging wildlife. It is so often those human activities that have been undertaken for other reasons that have by sheer chance done most to aid or damage our wild habitat.

Dew-ponds, garden ponds, ornamental ponds, village ponds and a variety of other types all fall into this heading of man-made dragonfly waters. Dew-ponds were once important places with a vital function in the lives of people, being the only source of water available on the Chalk hills, whilst village ponds were of far greater importance than mere decorative additions to the landscape. Before the days of piped water that is the norm today, the village pond was an indispensable part of life. Modern water supplies have made these ponds obsolete, but a few dew-ponds still exist and village ponds are still quite commonplace. Indeed, within the last few years, the National Trust has re-built a splendid dew-pond on the highest part of Stockbridge Down whilst an enthusiastic group of conservationists has refurbished the old village pond at Weeke on the outskirts of Winchester. Similar work on reclaiming village ponds that had become overgrown or used as tips for unwanted rubbish has been carried out at a number of other sites in Hampshire.

As standards of living have risen and people have more to spend on such luxuries, the number of garden ponds has mushroomed. Excessive populations of fish in such ponds do not help the cause of dragonflies, but such ponds have become an important habitat that is found on all of Hampshire's rock types, though they are perhaps of most importance on the Chalk because they often provide the only water in an area. Typical of this type of situation is the area surrounding the Editor's house in Winchester, which being situated on Chalk hills would naturally be completely devoid of surface water. There should be no breeding dragonflies there, only immature and adult dragonflies that have left water for the process of maturation or passing migrants. In fact, within a radius of 200 metres there is an old garden swimming pool that has been turned into a pond for wildlife, a tiny garden pond that was built with the specific purpose of attracting wildlife, and the aforementioned refurbished village pond at Weeke. All three waters have populations of dragonflies and damselflies that frequently visit the Editor's garden. The species concerned in these three ponds and their numbers will be mentioned in the part of this book that deals with habitat types in detail; suffice here to say that a year's population of dragonflies breeding on the three pools would run into a few hundred, and this in an area that would otherwise be a dragonfly Sahara. In the Systematic List of Species section, some examples of hatchings from small garden ponds are given under the heading of Southern Hawker.

Ornamental ponds exist for a wide variety of reasons. Nurseries and garden centres often have such a pool; some golf courses contain pools as water hazards; ponds are created as water supplies for small industries. In the Exbury Gardens, a series of pools have been constructed for irrigation of the area, fed by spring water from underground, and these pools have a considerable population of dragonflies.

Take this type of man-made habitat over the whole of Hampshire and we have a source of suitable water that is of considerable importance and growing in volume. Of course, many such ponds may be very transient in nature and may not represent a reliable habitat over a period of time, but as we pay more and more attention to our surrounds, ornamental ponds may well be a dragonfly habitat of major importance, especially if the current enthusiasm for gardening and home improvements continues, and it shows no signs of slowing if one judges by the amount of time given to the topic on television programmes. If more people came to look upon dragonflies as wholly harmless and attractive additions to their gardens, we may even have garden ponds being dug with that end as the main objective.

THE BASINGSTOKE CANAL There can be no doubt that this extensive area represents one of the most important dragonfly sites in the county. It has been studied in considerable detail by a number of observers and as dragonflies are found throughout its length, this man-made feature must have had a profoundly positive effect on their populations in that area. The insects are not confined to the bankside vegetation; neighbouring vegetation is used by sub-adults and roosting insects moving away from the water, whilst tree-tops along the banks are the places to which mating Downy Emeralds head to escape the attention of other males. The canal changes in character along its Hampshire length, and as the habitat changes so do the dragonfly species, a point that will be taken up more fully when the canal is treated in much greater detail in the following text.

NATURE RESERVES As public interest and awareness of the wild environment have come so much to the forefront in recent decades, so Nature Reserves have sprung up in all parts of Hampshire, run by a number of organisations. Few of these have had dragonflies as their main priority, but the habitat created or managed at such places as Titchfield

Haven, Botley Wood, Swanwick and the Itchen Valley Country Park, to name but four examples, has often benefited this order of insects. Such Reserves have already been mentioned on a previous page.

As for the negative side, in the same way that most of the good dragonfly habitat that we have created has been accidental, so none of the damage that we have done over the past two centuries has been with the deliberate intent of destroying wildlife of any kind.

DRAINAGE OF WETLANDS In the New Forest there has been relatively little major drainage compared with similar habitat in Europe, although the mires have suffered to some extent and these were key places for specialist dragonfly species such as the Scarce Blue-tailed Damselfly. Colin Tubbs, in his excellent volume *The New Forest* (Tubbs, 1986) gives a wealth of information on drainage damage in the New Forest mires, which are wet areas of heath that exist along valley bottoms and on hillsides below seepages. Tubbs considers the mires to be amongst the prime dragonfly sites of the Forest. Apparently there are 90 separate mires in the New Forest and no more than 20 in the remaining lowlands of England. Moreover, the New Forest mires are of international importance because they have not been so badly damaged as those in other parts of Europe. Tubbs writes: "The Forest mires are of enormous ecological importance because they are relatively undamaged and provide some of the best examples of this habitat known in Europe. Few valley mires have survived elsewhere in lowland Europe and most of those which remain have been subjected to artificial drainage, eutrophication from agricultural fertilizer runoff and other sources, and piecemeal reclamation" (Tubbs, 1986a). However, some drainage has taken place in Forest mires and damage done to this fragile habitat. Such drainage dates back to the mid-19th century and schemes were still taking place in the 1960s, 70s, 80s and 90s. Tubbs personally traced the 1923–1930 drains in the field and considers that although damage was done to the plant and invertebrate communities, "In no case did this savage treatment….completely succeed in destroying them, but it….must have indirectly destroyed many of the plants and invertebrates" (Tubbs, 1986b). In Colin's knowledgeable opinion, the most disastrous cases of drainage were of mires flanking Avon Water "which were the most extensive to be drained, even then known to be biologically among the richest…" (Tubbs, 1986c), whilst the drainage of Denny Bog between 1967 and 1981 also resulted in serious loss of excellent habitat. Dragonflies would, of course, have been amongst the invertebrates that suffered losses from this drainage, the extent being unknown due to the lack of quantitative data from pre-drainage days. Forest Enterprise and English Nature are very aware of this damage and regard refurbishment of the mires as one of their main priorities in the Forest. From the dragonfly viewpoint, the worst aspect of mire drainage is that the species to suffer most are those with highly specific needs that the mires satisfied, such as the Scarce Blue-tailed Damselfly. They had nowhere else to go in the Forest when that habitat was damaged and were therefore confined to the mires that remained suitable.

However, in terms of sheer acreage, the loss of habitat by draining the Forest mires would have been insignificant compared to the loss of wet heathland habitat that disappeared with the building of towns, roads, railways and other trappings of civilisation that necessitated the drainage and reclamation of such land on the Tertiary rocks. On the Tertiary rocks of north-east Hampshire, the great bogs of Bracknell's Bottom, Birch Bottom, Yateley Heath Wood, Hawley Peatmoor, Sheepmoor, Fleet Peatmoor, Pyestock Bottom, Cove Common and Crookham Heath have all been drained or have dried out and become overgrown. It is not unreasonable to suppose that some specialist species that are now distributed very locally in Hampshire, such as Small Red Damselfly or even Scarce Blue-tailed Damselfly, bred in these areas when they still provided suitable habitat, although such a statement is supposition and cannot be stated as fact. However, it is almost certain that less specialist species were once resident in some strength in the localities named in this paragraph.

On the chalklands there was very little to drain, and since this rock accounts for around 45% of Hampshire's area, depending on whether or not one counts chalk with superficial deposits, it follows that most of the county has not experienced the wholesale drainage of suitable dragonfly habitat that has occurred in so many English shires. There was a certain amount of drainage in the main river valleys that traverse the Chalk, because before they were tamed, these Hampshire rivers wandered across their valley floors in systems of braided courses and these were brought to heel as the streams were freed from choking vegetation and the water channelled into more orderly routes.

TOWNS, ROADS, RAILWAYS AND OTHER DEVELOPMENTS The building of Southampton, Portsmouth, Aldershot, Basingstoke and other towns that are built on the Tertiary rocks must have resulted in a considerable loss of wet heathland and forest habitat, and the damage to dragonflies will never be known with any degree of accuracy because most of this development was so far back in the past there is no information on the type of habitat that was lost. Although such towns must certainly hold smaller populations of these insects than would have been the case when they were wild country, they are not dragonfly deserts. Attention has already been drawn to the considerable supply of habitat that results from the construction of garden ponds, ornamental town ponds and such waters, and these have to a probably small extent offset the loss of habitat resulting from town and road building.

NEGLECT Some excellent dragonfly habitat has been lost or damaged by neglect, not only at natural sites but also at sites that were man-made. Parts of the Basingstoke Canal have suffered in this way and now support fewer species than was the case when they were in their prime. The text has also drawn attention to Sable Pond and its rescue by Brian and Jean Sutton from utter neglect. Village ponds have often become dumping grounds for the unwanted detritus of modern living and there is always this danger that a site providing suitable dragonfly habitat will deteriorate due to neglect and become overgrown or so filled with mud that it ceases to be of value to Odonata. It is to be hoped that the growing awareness of conservation may go some way to preventing such neglect and fortunately a great deal of our best dragonfly habitat is situated in nature reserves or areas where local conservationists are actively involved.

RECREATION However, neglect can take many forms and waters that have suffered neglect from the wildlife point of view are not just those that have stagnated, become choked with unwanted vegetation or generally decayed. Not everyone would agree that wildlife is the main priority on water areas and recreational interests are powerful competitors. Boating and fishing are not always compatible with conservation and although devotees of such interests would strongly refute suggestions that their interests have led to water areas being neglected, from the point of view of wildlife neglect may well have taken place, however smart and pristine the waters may appear. The Avon valley between Ringwood and Fordingbridge hosts a number of disused gravel pits, some of which are havens for wildlife of many forms. Others, however, have boating or fishing as their major priorities and although they may look very attractive to the human eye, they offer limited opportunities for wildlife. As recreation booms, this threat to dragonfly habitat could well adversely influence valuable areas.

AGRICULTURE There must be areas of the northern and southern Tertiary rocks that have been reclaimed for agriculture that, in their natural state, held dragonfly populations. However, most agricultural development in those area happened so far back in the past that we have no real idea of what species were inhabiting such habitat before agriculture took over and we can only vaguely state that farming might have brought about some losses in Odonata populations. Most of the rocks in these Tertiary areas develop poor soils from the farming point of view.

POLLUTION We have little positive evidence of the adverse effects that various sources of pollution have had on dragonfly populations. Such pollution comes from a number of sources that range from agricultural fertilizers or waste from rubbish tips, to pollution from roads and industry. Serious leaks of pollutants have definitely occurred, such as the accidental discharge of sewage into the Moors River that may have been the last nail in the coffin of the Orange-spotted Emerald in our country (see 'Lost Species' – Orange-spotted Emerald in Part Four). Since the 1970s, agricultural fertilizers draining into the Basingstoke Canal at Greywell are thought to have changed the water chemistry and this may have had an adverse influence on dragonflies, whilst A.W. Richards suggested that the army's use of insecticides at Fleet Pond in the late 1940s to control mosquitoes might have led to the disappearance of the Small Red Damselfly and the Scarce Blue-tailed Damselfly at that site (see the species account of the Scarce Blue-tailed Damselfly in the Part Four 'Systematic List of Species').

However, all this is conjecture, but the likelihood is that some Odonata sites have been damaged by the increasing amount of pollution that has been taking place in Britain.

AFFORESTATION As with the previous heading, we can only surmise what the influence of afforestation has been on the dragonfly population because we have no definite data on conditions before afforestation took place. On the chalk, any forestry development must have had only a very marginal influence on Odonata populations because, as the previous text has said, chalk hills are not naturally good dragonfly habitat, but on the other rocks in Hampshire there may have been a quite considerable detrimental influence over a long period of time. Certainly on the northern Tertiary rocks, some of the wet heathland that has been converted to forest must have suffered, especially where the forestry has been in the form of dense coniferous plantations. Here, we simply draw attention to afforestation as a possible threat to dragonfly habitat.

It would therefore seem that human activities have had both beneficial and detrimental results of considerable proportions on dragonfly populations, although the balance of good or bad is a subject for debate. Our task as conservationists is to see that we prevent the position from deteriorating and, if possible, make Hampshire more suitable for this quite harmless and fascinating order of insects.

PART THREE

HABITATS

This section classifies habitats according to location within the county, that is the Tertiary rocks of the south, the Tertiaries of the north, the main river valleys, the Basingstoke Canal, the coast, the chalklands and the Wealden rocks near the Surrey border.

THE NEW FOREST AND OTHER AREAS OF TERTIARY ROCKS IN SOUTHERN HAMPSHIRE
The New Forest occupies a major portion of the Hampshire Basin, which is situated centrally on the south coast of England immediately opposite the Isle of Wight. Geologically it is composed of Tertiary deposits laid down over the millennia by rivers and alternately rising and falling sea levels. Because of its acidic nature the New Forest and the adjoining Dorset heaths are more akin to high moorland and seem out of place amongst the surrounding chalk, clays and greensands. This is its major strength; the position it occupies in England probably enjoys the most equable climate and seldom suffers the particular low winter temperatures normally associated with this type of habitat. This allows many species to thrive which otherwise would not. Dragonflies also exhibit a greater species diversity in habitats that are slightly acidic, with a pH of 5.5–6.0. These two factors, when further combined with the three main ecotypes of lowland heath, valley mire and pasture woodland in close proximity, make the New Forest a particularly valuable area within a European context. It is the valley mires that are of major consequence to dragonflies. The great majority of the mires have central water courses and because of this they not only exhibit the usual acidic characteristics in the mire itself but what nutrient there is leaches into the water course so raising the pH and its plant feeding value. Where the underlying geology is favourable, this can be quite significant.

Topographically, the New Forest is composed of very gently tilting strata that rise towards the north at an angle of just a few degrees The beds, in decreasing order of age, are the Bagshot, Bracklesham, Barton and Hamstead Beds with the younger strata eroded from the north to reveal the older rocks. The angle of slope is so gentle that it would barely show on a sketch section.

The Bagshot and Bracklesham Beds of the north are more acidic than the more base-enriched Barton and Hamstead Beds of the south, but this is a gross over-simplification of the area's geology and the situation on the ground is much more complex with pockets of acidic and base-enriched strata occurring locally within close proximity of one another, and much dependent upon local variations in ground level.

The main Southampton/Ringwood road, the A31, runs from east to west along the main watershed and effectively divides the New Forest into north and south sub-compartments. To the north the landscape is more exposed and rugged with a series of steep-sided river valleys, separated by gravel-capped ridges, that traverse the region from east to west with the streams flowing towards the River Avon in the west. Here sands and gravels dominate the area, making the substrate porous and allowing the numerous small streams to reduce in volume quite dramatically in most summers. In extended hot spells there is very little flow and many streams are reduced to isolated pools separated by long lengths of bare, dry, gravel bed. To the south of the A31 watershed the ground falls away quite steeply towards a massive, uninterrupted block of forestry Inclosures that effectively form a micro-climatological divide between north and south. This block is of fairly recent origin when, after the Deer Removal Act of 1851, the isolated Inclosures occupying this tract were extended and joined together. South of the Inclosures the area is dominated by low, gently undulating heath all the way to the Solent shoreline. In this region all of the streams flow from north to south with the major ones rising on the watershed.

Much of the wind in early spring comes from the north and north-east, sweeping down the relatively barren nature of the northern Forest with unimpeded access from the chalk downs. This cooling effectively prevents the waters from warming quickly when compared with much of the rest of southern England. The net effect of this is that invertebrate emergence can be two or three weeks late in comparison with most of southern England. This is not so in the region south of the block of Inclosures as the Inclosures themselves provide an effective barrier, and when this is allied to the temperature-ameliorating influence of the sea, there is a noticeable difference in emergence times when the southern New Forest is compared with the north.

In Victorian times, and in fact until 1939 and the outbreak of World War II, the New Forest was a Mecca for insect collectors, including those interested in dragonflies. In those days the area was famed for the fauna of its streams, notably rare species being the Club-tailed Dragonfly, Southern Damselfly and Scarce Blue-tailed Damselfly. In addition, because of the proximity of habitats, two scarce species more associated with moorland could also be found cohabiting here, these being the Keeled Skimmer and the Small Red Damselfly.

The situation has now changed. Various drainage schemes, beginning with labour intensive hand reclamation in the late 1920s and early 1930s and culminating with more adventurous mechanical drainage in the 1950s and 1960s, has very much changed the character of all the larger southern streams and a few of the mires. After this, further drainage schemes arose under compromise as a result of the tensions between the various bodies responsible for one aspect or another of New Forest development. The Verderers, on the one hand, were responsible to the Commoners – those who own the ponies and cattle grazing the open Forest – and had to provide adequate grazing for their animals. It was seen by them that the natural expansion of the mires and prolonged inundation of the lawns adjacent to the streams by floodwaters limited the available grazing. On the other hand the nature conservation lobby, headed by English Nature, took a different view in that they wished to preserve the natural integrity of the Forest and opposed much drainage. There can be little doubt that the early schemes had an extremely detrimental effect on the fauna of these streams. The most notable effects are the complete disappearance of the Club-tailed Dragonfly and the almost complete disappearance of the White-legged Damselfly that is now restricted to small numbers in one very confined locality.

However, still water has proliferated in the last 60 years beyond all recognition. There are very few natural ponds of any size in the New Forest, exceptions being Whitten Pond and Long Pond, both near Burley, and possibly Green Pond near Fritham, and Whitten Pond has been enlarged by a man-made dam at the exit stream. Early literature mentions three ponds of note. Eyeworth Pond, near Fritham, was constructed in the early 18th century to provide water for a gunpowder factory. It was, and still is, known for its populations of Downy Emeralds and Red-eyed Damselflies. It is probably true to say that this is the only pond on the open Forest to support a viable population of the latter species, although this population was severely threatened by the introduction of large numbers of wildfowl in the early 1980s. Sowley Pond is the largest in the region; it is wholly on private land and not accessible, although it is within the New Forest boundary. It was constructed to power two hammer mills to smelt the iron ore collected locally. Sowley held the only Forest population of the Variable Damselfly, and as it is now inaccessible to observers, the species may no longer be there. The third of these ponds no longer exists; this was a flight pond immediately above Dog Kennel Bridge on the Burley Lodge estate which has long since been drained.

Another area of note was Malborough Deeps, near Holmsley, a series of small ponds left after extensive diggings for marl which is a loamy clay used for the construction of 'cob and wattle' cottages and also as a substitute for lime on fields. The Hairy Dragonfly was reputed to occur here in numbers, but many decades of scrub incursion have rendered much of the area wholly unsuitable. What is surprising, by current conditions, is that Hatchet Pond is only mentioned as being barren and devoid of interest; it was also used to power another hammer mill in the late 18th century. It ceases to be surprising when viewed from the beginning of the 19th century. Photographs from that period indicate a total lack of aquatic vegetation with little or no trees and scrub around the now abundantly vegetated north-eastern tip. It is still quite true that the greater portion of Hatchet Pond has very little interest for Odonata, but there can be few places within the Forest in early summer that can provide a more varied and splendid display of dragonflies than the northern tip of Hatchet. The reason that the vegetation is restricted to this small area is that the construction of the pond was accomplished by flooding a series of gravel and marl pits and that the marl pits were confined to this small area. In addition, the northern bank has numerous boggy runnels draining into it and this provides an atypical (non-wooded) habitat for Downy Emeralds.

Beaulieu Estate, in the extreme south of the New Forest, was originally part of the hunting forest decreed by William the First, but was subsequently gifted to the church by a subsequent head of state. It is now wholly private and owned by Lord Montagu and the important dragonfly pools around Blackwater will be dealt with in the coastal section of habitat types. Otherwise, the estate is significant because when occupied as a monastery, the monks constructed a series of ponds for rearing fish. At the head of a small stream a short series of hatching tanks were constructed and these led to three further ponds, each increasing in size and volume downstream. The two largest ponds are now prime dragonfly sites. Middle Pond, as it is known, has a good breeding population of Hairy Dragonflies whilst the largest, Bowman's Pond, which is now well managed for recreational fishing, has a dense breeding population of Downy Emeralds and Red-eyed Damselflies. This concludes an outline of the still waters prior to the 1940s.

During World War II, German bombers dropped unused bombs as they left England. Many of these landed in the New Forest, particularly in the north, and have resulted in small but valuable aquatic habitats in their own right. This was the beginning of what was to become a massive expansion of small to medium-sized still waters over the next 25 years. It was only after 1945 that

Two of the most important dragonfly streams in Britain. Crockford Stream in the New Forest (ABOVE) © *John Taverner* and (BELOW) the Itchen Valley Country Park © *Alan Hold*, both areas holding populations of Southern Damselflies that run into four figures.

(ABOVE) Eyeworth Pond (Irons Well) in the New Forest, one of Hampshire's main sites for the Red-eyed Damselfly, and (BELOW) the corner of Hatchet Pond – also in the New Forest – where a number of species breed, including Downy Emeralds © *John Taverner*.

(ABOVE) Latchmoor Brook, a typical New Forest stream where Golden-ringed Dragonflies find an ideal habitat, and (BELOW) Sable Water, one of our finest dragonfly sites, that was only discovered in 2001 and saved from development plans to tip waste nearby on a large scale © *John Taverner.*

(ABOVE) Part of the short stretch of Ober Water, in the New Forest, where White-legged Damselflies retain a tenuous foothold in southern Hampshire. (BELOW) Toby's Pond, one of the many man-made waters in the county that support a considerable population and range of Odonata © *John Taverner*.

mechanisation gained a strong foothold in the forestry industry. Lorries replaced the horse and cart, timber was in short supply and the forestry began to expand rapidly. This expansion in the New Forest resulted in what are known as the Verderers' Inclosures, short-term, one-crop plantings of quick-growing trees. Forest roads were required that would take the weight of a lorry, both in the new and old Inclosures, and roads in the old Inclosures had to be reinforced and widened. The Forestry Commission accomplished this task by utilising the gravel capping so prevalent on heath lands. Old pits were expanded and new ones excavated, and as they fell into disuse they quickly became colonised both by plants and aquatic fauna. Notable examples of these are at Holmsley and in Highland Water Inclosure.

In the 1960s the then Deputy Surveyor, Arthur Cadman, had a number of flight ponds excavated, within or at the head of some of the valley mires, to attract wild duck. These have subsequently proved to be particularly valuable for dragonflies; for example, at its peak in the 1980s, Broomy Pond had the highest species count of any single habitat in the New Forest.

The continuing expansion of building work around the periphery of the New Forest has led to bigger and better lakes as gravel extraction exhausts the supply of gravel in one place and moves on. The lakes left behind quickly become colonised and have provided a hitherto missing ecotype that has attracted species previously considered rare in the area. Of note are the Brown Hawker, the Migrant Hawker and the Ruddy Darter, all of which now frequent the Forest to greater or lesser extents in setting up at least temporary breeding colonies. It is worth remembering that the larger ponds within the local vicinity are vital to some species as they harbour large active breeding colonies that act as a nucleus from which expansion can and does take place and, being larger bodies of water, are not as susceptible to drying out or pollution.

There are now well over 300 documented still water sites in the New Forest. As with all man-made ponds, the tendency is to revert, silt up, and for the periphery to become ringed with scrub. In the absence of management it is unlikely that many of the smaller ponds will have a lifespan exceeding three decades. To maintain a 'best' balance of vegetation requires frequent minor adjustments which is both time-consuming and costly, so it is inevitable that many of the ponds are now in less than ideal condition.

In 1984, Noelle and Tony Welstead produced a booklet entitled *The Dragonflies of the New Forest*. Those fortunate enough to own a copy will find it contains much useful information, but it is not easy to come by a copy today.

THE TERTIARY ROCKS OF NORTHERN HAMPSHIRE

To some extent, the Tertiary rocks of northern Hampshire give habitat that is similar to the New Forest, but without The Forest's protection that stems from it being Crown Land, this area of northern Hampshire has seen much development and the heathland habitat has disappeared under urban expansion, military use, road building and other 'improvements'. The area still possesses excellent dragonfly habitat, especially along the Basingstoke Canal and in the many lakes and pools that exist in the area, but it lacks the unbroken expanse of prime habitat that is found in the New Forest.

THE MAIN RIVER VALLEYS (THE TEST, ITCHEN, AVON AND MOORS RIVER)

The majority of the rivers of Hampshire, except those on the New Forest, have been under-recorded for Odonata. The closely guarded fishing interests of the major chalk rivers and adjacent fishing lakes have prevented regular monitoring. It is hoped that the recent co-operation of both fishermen and land owners will continue, thereby improving the knowledge and understanding of the dragonflies associated with our rivers and the other water courses within their river valley systems. The right to protect the fishing interests by riparian owners is acknowledged and therefore it is strongly recommended that surveys of sensitive areas be conducted only as part of a scheme agreed with the riparian owner and supported by recognised conservation authorities such as English Nature or the Environment Agency.

The faster flowing rivers, when compared with lakes, ponds or canals, do not support a great diversity of Odonata species. However, dragonfly recorders are reminded that monitoring of these water courses can bring its own rewards; imagine the delight for those finding a small colony of Scarce Chaser on the River Wey, near Bentley. There is much yet to be learned of the dragonflies and damselflies of the Hampshire rivers.

The Hampshire rivers may be grouped into four systems.
1. The southern Tertiary rivers
2. The New Forest rivers
3. The north and eastern rivers
4. The southern chalk rivers

1. The main southern Tertiary rivers are the Hamble, Wallington and Alver that all drain into the eastern Solent. The Tertiary deposits of sand and clay are less permeable than chalk and therefore run-off occurs quickly after rainfall. The flow of these rivers is very variable and flooding is liable in the low-lying areas.
2. Most of the acidic New Forest streams drain the sands, gravel and peat and either flow west to the Avon or, like the Beaulieu and Lymington Rivers, flow directly into the Solent. The most notable of these include the Avon Water, Black Water, Crockford Stream, Highland Water, Dockens Water, Latchmore Brook and Ober Water. As these are covered in the New Forest section of 'Habitat', they will be omitted from this section.
3. The northern and eastern rivers include the Enborne, Loddon, Whitewater, Blackwater and Wey that flow through Berkshire and Surrey to the Thames, whilst the Rother flows through West Sussex to join the Arun. The Loddon, Whitewater and the northern branch of the Wey all rise on chalk but soon flow over London or Gault Clay, their water thereby progressively losing its clarity along the way. The clearer water of the southern Wey is somewhat acid as it originates from the heaths of the Woolmer Forest area. The Rother is the only Hampshire Greensand river.
4. The southern chalk rivers of England are important on an international context because they represent a significant proportion of this river type in the whole of Europe. Of these rivers, only the Itchen and the Test are considered as having the 'classic' Chalk river communities described in published river type classifications. The other major river that drains from the central chalk downland of the county is the Meon. The source of the River Avon is in the Wiltshire Downs with much of its lower reaches, from Fordingbridge to Christchurch, forming the modern county boundary with Dorset. Prior to local government reorganisation in 1974, the lower reaches of Moors River were within the administrative county of Hampshire. As this book covers the vice-counties 11 and 12, records from this area of the Moors River are included.

These southern chalk rivers generally lie in shallow basins of Chalk, a rock rich in many of the nutrients required for plant growth. Rain rapidly percolates through the rock so that there is little surface run-off, and in consequence serious flooding is rare. The flows on these rivers are almost entirely spring-fed and therefore are fairly stable in terms of seasonal fluctuations and temperatures. The well oxygenated water from these chalk springs is typically clear, rich in plant nutrients and at a constant temperature of around 10°C with a pH between 7.5 and 8.5. The clarity of the Hampshire chalk rivers is maintained by the excess of calcium removing sufficient nitrates and phosphates from solution to prevent the growth of phytoplankton, microscopic green algae. The bed substrate is predominately flint gravels, with silt being distributed according to the nature of the channel, its flow and management. This combination provides the ideal range of conditions for the *Ranunculus* community, which gives many of these the rivers the status of a candidate Special Area of Conservation (cSAC). It is the adjacent bankside and floodplain habitats of the Itchen and Test that support strong populations of Southern Damselfly.

It has been suggested that the paucity of dragonfly records from the main chalk streams has nothing or little to do with pH values but is the result of the temperature regime of the water. Being spring fed, they are cooler than heathland streams throughout the warmer months and it is possible that this temperature regime is unfavourable for dragonflies. This relative scarcity of dragonflies in the chalk river valleys, and whether it is due to pH values, water temperatures or other factors, is a feature that would repay serious research.

An account of the Hampshire chalk rivers would not be complete without reference to the water-meadows for which the county is famous. Records indicate that water-meadows were being established at the beginning of the 17th century. By the early 19th century water-meadows were in widespread use on the Avon, Test, Itchen, Anton and Meon, and could also be found on their main tributaries. Water-meadows were highly managed systems which used the relatively warm, nutrient-rich water from the chalk to irrigate the grassland to encourage an early spring growth of grass and subsequent hay crops that were of such critical importance to the economy of local sheep farming.

It is considered that the formation of the water-meadows and their subsequent management is the greatest single factor in shaping the way the river valleys are today. Evidence, in the form of carriers, weirs and hatches of these abandoned water-meadows can still be found alongside the main chalk rivers. The meadows and their associated channels are now valuable refuges for wildlife and it is in these partly derelict water systems along the Test and Itchen that the populations of the Southern Damselfly are found.

The Test – The River Test rises as a spring in a field east of Overton close to the hamlet of Ashe. The river is soon fully established as it flows south-west past Overton and through Laverstoke and Whitchurch. It is interesting that three damselfly species, Large Red,

Blue-tailed and Azure, have been recorded within the first 100 m of the source. There are no other records of dragonfly species for these upper reaches until the river reaches Wherwell, and it would be interesting to carry out more research in this stretch to discover the true situation.

The Test is braided, constantly dividing into loops and channels that rejoin the parent river. It is fed throughout its length by a number of tributaries carrying water from the surrounding chalk downs. The first of these tributaries is the Bourne Rivulet that rises not far from borders of Wiltshire and Berkshire to flow through St Mary Bourne and Hurstbourne Priors and join the Test just below Whitchurch. The River Dever is the only major tributary that joins the Test from the east, rising near the A33 road from Southampton to Basingstoke to flow through Micheldever, past Sutton Scotney and Barton Stacey to join a mass of channels of the Test near Wherwell. A random survey of three visits to approximately 500 m of the river and adjacent water-meadows near Wherwell in 1998 revealed only two species, Banded Demoiselle and Blue-tailed Damselfly.

The Anton begins life as two small tributaries that soon join to form the main Anton River by the time it reaches Andover. The river flows close to a small complex of lakes, known as the Anton Lakes, to the north of Andover and past several other lakes on the south of the town to join the River Test at Fullerton, close to the 'The Mayfly ' inn.

After flowing between the villages of Wherwell and Chilbolton, the Test, with its various channels, continues its journey through Leckford and the famous Longstock Water Gardens to reach Stockbridge. A survey of Chilbolton Common in 1998 found only four species, these being Banded Demoiselle, Blue-tailed Damselfly, Common Darter and a single Azure Damselfly, but another observer around the same date added two male Golden-ringed Dragonflies to that list. An ongoing survey of Longstock Water Gardens has to date revealed nine species, including Black-tailed Skimmer, Golden-ringed Dragonfly and Broad-bodied Chaser.

South of Stockbridge the waters of the Test are fished by members of the celebrated Houghton Club, reputed to be one of the most exclusive clubs of its kind in the world. Adjacent to the Test and its complex of channels are several lakes stocked with fish. Just south of Houghton, the Test is joined by the Wallop Brook that began life close to the Wiltshire border at Over Wallop.

Monitoring for the Southern Damselfly located a strong colony south of Stockbridge in 1998 on secondary carriers and ditches. Other species included, Banded Demoiselle, Azure Damselfly and Golden-ringed Dragonfly. Surveys near Pittleworth and at Timsbury have recorded six common species, including Blue-tailed Damselfly, Common Blue Damselfy and Common Darter.

South of Mottisfont, at Dunbridge, the Test is joined by the River Dun, carrying water from over the Wiltshire border. The various channels of the Test now enter Romsey and reform into the main river as it flows past Broadlands House. A randomly selected site near Romsey was found to support only five common species, including Blue-tailed Damselfly and Common Darter. The Test then continues its journey through the Lower Test Nature Reserve to discharge into the Southampton Water near Totton.

It can be seen from the above that there is much of the Test and the other water bodies within the river valley yet to be surveyed, including lakes near Whitchurch, Houghton and Broadlands.

The Itchen – The River Itchen has its permanent source in a roadside field near Bramdean in the Hampshire Downs and flows through Winchester and Eastleigh before discharging into the Southampton Water. Some 6.5 km downstream from this source, the Itchen is joined by two substantial tributaries, the Arle and the Candover Brook, whilst a number of tiny streams join the main river in its middle and lower reaches. The whole river, including its headwater tributaries, was notified as a SSSI in 1996 for its chalk stream habitat, including flora, invertebrates, fish, birds and mammals. Most of this SSSI is a SAC for its Common Water-crowfoot and Southern Damselfly populations, along with Atlantic Salmon, Bullhead, and Brook Lamprey, European Otter and White-clawed Crayfish.

From its source, the Itchen flows through the village of Cheriton and the small country town of Alresford. In the 12th century, the Bishop of Winchester wished to make the Itchen a navigable waterway from Winchester to Southampton, and in order to maintain an even flow of water he created a large pond at Alresford by means of a dam, the pond acting as a supply of water that could be tapped if the waterway from Winchester to Southampton became too shallow in dry spells. Alresford Pond has now shrunk to around a third of its size, and it has been well studied for its birds and flora, but few dragonfly records have been submitted. This pond, along with others in Alrebury Park, may well be worth monitoring for Odonata.

The river then flows through the villages of Itchen Stoke and Itchen Abbas and past Avington House with its lake, which is also under-recorded for Odonata. There are no lakes in the valley where the Itchen flows through the villages of Martyr Worthy, King's Worthy and Abbots Worthy, an area celebrated for its watercress production.

On the outskirts of Winchester, the Itchen flows through Winnall Moors Nature Reserve, which is managed by the Hampshire and Isle of Wight Wildlife Trust. Consequently, Odonata records are a little more complete for this stretch, although the habitat is unlikely to produce a large number of species due to the lack of pools and ponds in the valley floor. As it passes through the city, the river again has limited habitat to support a wide variety of species, but as it flows towards Eastleigh it moves through Itchen Valley Country Park where over 15 species have been recorded.

In the past, a network of water-meadows was constructed in the valley below Winchester, through Twyford, Shawford, Brambridge, Bishopstoke and Stoneham. These meadows created a multiplicity of water courses in the valley, and although they were allowed to decline in the late 19th and early 20th centuries, it is in the remnants of those ditches and carriers where a steady flow of water is still maintained throughout the year and where an emergent vegetation exists, that the Southern Damselfly can be found. Research conducted in 2001 estimates the population in the Itchen Valley Country Park to be in the order of several thousands, making it one of the most important sites within Britain, and possibly Europe, for this globally threatened damselfly. Recent surveys show that the Southern Damselfly can be found in suitable streams and ditches from Twyford Moors to the southern boundaries of the Itchen Valley Country Park.

The river then passes under the M27, through Woodmill and under Cobden Bridge, to enter the city of Southampton and on to Southampton Water.

The Avon – The River Avon, with its diverse flora and fauna, is regarded as one of the finest examples of a British Chalk stream. The large range of habitats within its flood plain include herb-rich meadows and pastures, fens and mires, dune grassland, woods and heathland.

The Avon rises near Pewsey in Wiltshire as a series of small streams fed by chalk springs. It flows through Wiltshire where it is met by tributaries, such as the Rivers Nadder and Wylye, around Salisbury. In its lower reaches, it flows over acidic sands and clays. South of Fordingbridge, the Dockens water and other acid streams from the New Forest drain into the Avon.

As it has meandered over the millennia, it has created ox-bows, gravel shallows and sluggish backwaters. This diversity of habitat supports a rich flora and fauna, a number of the species being rare and threatened. The river and its associated streams, dykes and nearby lakes sustain a wide range of dragonflies, including the Scarce Chaser.

The River Avon system has been designated as one of the first candidate Special Area of Conservation (cSAC) rivers in the UK. The SAC also includes Dockens Water, a largely unmodified stream draining New Forest heathlands. The importance of the Avon and its tributaries has been recognised for several internationally rare or threatened species such as Sea and Brook Lamprey, Bullhead, Atlantic Salmon and Desmoulin's Whorl Snail. The river is largely dominated by the Water-crowfoot vegetation community.

The lower stretches, covering approximately 1,383 hectares between Bickton and Christchurch Harbour, has been designated an SSSI. Within this designated area the Avon meanders over a broad flood plain that is dissected by a series of small streams and dykes. On both sides of the river the land rises to the heathlands of the New Forest and south-east Dorset.

Included in the northern section of the SSSI is the Blatchford Lakes complex, a series of lakes created by the excavation of aggregate from the river terraces, now managed by Wessex Water. These lakes and grasslands of the lower Avon Valley are included within the designation and they are nationally and internationally important for migratory wildfowl and waders. A range of leisure activities, such as sailing, water-skiing and fishing takes place on several of the lakes throughout the year. The lakes' dragonfly populations have not been extensively monitored, although such work has started and it is hoped that the recent provision of a Study Centre near Ivy Lake may give encouragement for future research.

Further information on this important site may be gained from the English Nature website, www.english.nature.org.uk.

The Moors River – The Moors River is no longer regarded as a Hampshire river as local government reorganisation in 1976 placed it in Dorset. However, as the river falls within the boundaries of VC 11, South Hampshire, it is included in this book. It rises from the chalk in Cranbourne Chase as the River Crane and becomes the Moors River at Ebblake after it enters the Tertiary deposits. The river is joined by several tributaries, the most important of which is the Udden Water, before it meets the River Stour at Blackwater. It flows through a landscape of low rolling hills with an irregular and enclosed patchwork of pasture, woodland and heathland on acid soils.

The diverse geology and water chemistry contributes to the river's rich flora and fauna. The Moors system was notified by English Nature as an SSSI in July 1999, which should protect it from a variety of practices that are likely to be damaging. The Dorset Wildlife Trust manages the 20 hectare Troublefield Nature Reserve, a wet grassland adjoining the river near Hurn.

The River Crane and the upper reaches of the Moors River has clear sparkling water with a clean bed, abundant aquatic vegetation and few signs of pollution. Unfortunately, the lower reaches suffered from pollution during the 1970s and 80s from sewage works, industrial development and possible agricultural chemical run-off. At that time the water in these lower reaches was considered to be opaque, and the bed and aquatic vegetation became covered with algae and silt (Prendergast, 1985).

The Moors River has long been known for its diverse dragonfly populations that include several nationally rare species, but "pollution problems have been the likely reason for their demise in recent years. The Scarce Chaser is one rarity that survives in the Moors River … The heathland SSSI adjacent to [it] also supports Small Red Damselfly and Scarce Blue-tailed Damselfly damselflies" (Dorset Local Environment Action Plan, Environment Agency, 1997).

A survey carried out in 1977 reported that, including historical and anecdotal records, 29 species of Odonata have been found in the Moors River area. This includes the Scarce Chaser, the Small Red, the Southern and the Scarce Blue-tailed Damselflies. It is claimed in the article "Dorset's Exquisite Chalk Streams" appearing on the Dorset Wildlife Trust website that at least 32 species have been recorded. Stretches of the Moors River were known as the major habitat for the Orange-spotted Emerald, now lost to Britain.

A survey of the stretch between Potterne Bridge, Verwood and St Leonard's Bridge in 1985 by Col E.D.V. Prendergast recorded 20 species. This did not include the Scarce Chaser that is found downstream of his survey area. The stretch of river between St Leonard's and Hurn was monitored by David Winsland in 1989 when he recorded 10 species, including the Scarce Chaser. David suggests that the small number of species in this study area may have been due to previous pollution and the shading out of sections of the river for significant parts of the day by dense woodland (Winsland, 1991).

Unfortunately, there have been few records for the Moors River during the past decade, so the current situation is unclear. It would appear that the river, at least in its lower stretches, might not now hold such a diversity of Odonata as it did during the early and mid parts of the last century. This might be, as suggested in several reports, due to pollution from both residential and industrial development and the lack of sympathetic management of the river and its environs.

THE BASINGSTOKE CANAL When a new canal was opened in 1794 linking the Hampshire market town of Basingstoke with the Wey Navigation in Surrey, it crossed a countryside that would be unrecognisable to a visitor today. Basingstoke in the 18th century was situated in a rich, fertile country of woods, pastures and the estates of the nobility and gentry (Defoe, 1724). It was the largest settlement on the route of the canal; all of the other modern towns on its banks were rural villages or hamlets dependent on farming.

The new canal would, via the Wey Navigation and the Thames, provide Basingstoke with the cheapest means of transport to and from the London markets. Construction began in October 1788 near the Surrey town of Weybridge and, simultaneously, on the digging of a tunnel through Greywell Hill in Hampshire. The route of the canal was to cross the great heath near a small village called Woking, then by way of Pirbright, Frimley Green and Ash before entering Hampshire near Aldershot. Continuing westwards it would pass through Crookham, Dogmersfield, Odiham, Nately and Basing, its total length being 50.7 kilometres. The first tolls were collected in 1791 in Surrey but it was not until December 1793 that the navigation was opened at Odiham Wharf. The new canal was fully opened to Basingstoke on 4th September 1794 (Vine, 1968).

The landscape through which the canal passed is the key to why it became so rich in wildlife and wetland plants. It Hampshire it crossed the flood plains of five rivers, the Loddon, Lyde, Whitewater, Hart and Blackwater, as well as a number of lesser streams. These would all have been bordered by wet pastures or fens, including Basing Peatmoor beside the Loddon, Mapledurwell Fen and Andwell Moors associated with the Lyde and the Greywell Moors/Warnborough Marshes complex beside the Whitewater, now a Hampshire and Isle of Wight Wildlife Trust nature reserve and SSSI. In the farmscape of the 1790s, dissected by many small watercourses, wet meadows would have been the norm, but very few remain today. Crookham Peatmoor, adjacent to the canal beside the River Hart, was drained and converted to agricultural grassland as recently as 1991.

At Crookham the landscape changed dramatically from fields and copses to a treeless terrain of heathland commons, bogs, peat moors and pools. Of the 37 kilometres of canal between Crookham and the Wey Navigation, some 32 kilometres were across heathland. The modern town of Fleet did not exist and the urban sprawl of Rushmoor Borough was undreamed of by the inhabitants of the villages of Aldershot and Farnborough. Wet heathland, peatmoors and mires were a feature of this landscape, including Zephon Common and Coxheath, the vast Crookham Common, Fleet Pond (at that time, a lake at least double its size today), Crookham Bog, Eelmoor Marsh and the bogs of Cove Common, and further areas of wet heathland at Rushmoor Bottom and Smallshott Bottom. Several tributaries of the Hart and the Blackwater rose on these commons. In Surrey, the heathlands bordered the canal almost continuously from Ash to the great bog at Sheerwater, famous for its dragonflies until destroyed for housing development in 1949.

The promoters of the canal had been optimistic about its commercial prospects. By completion, construction costs had exceeded their estimates by 50% and in only three years throughout its history as a commercial waterway did the canal achieve the predicted tonnage. The disappointing returns were worsened by water shortages during periods of drought, increased competition as a result of improvement to the roads of Hampshire and then from the opening of the London to Basingstoke railway in 1839 and the line through Ash Vale and Aldershot a decade later (Vine, 1994).

Attempts to revive the canal's fortunes met with limited success and at times maintenance was neglected. By 1900 locks were in a poor state of repair, obstructions such as fallen trees were not attended to and the canal west of Odiham was "much overgrown with weeds". Commercial barge traffic had ceased by 1904 on the upper reaches of the canal, though continued from Aldershot and in Surrey. Some sections were maintained for rowing boat hire. Photographs of the canal from around the turn of the century show

Figure 6. The course and habitat of the Basingstoke Canal
Map produced by HBIC with special thanks to Purgle Linham and Nicky Court

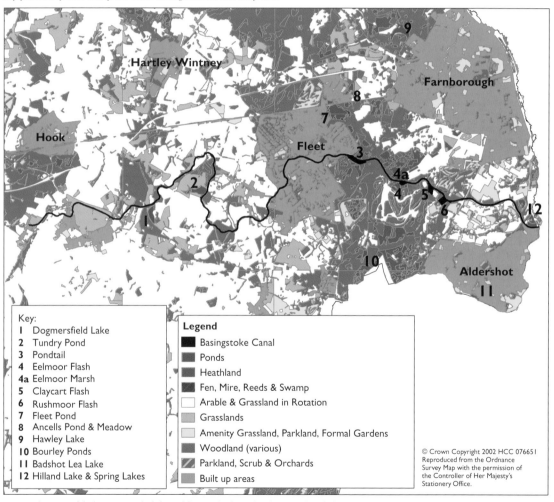

Key:
1   Dogmersfield Lake
2   Tundry Pond
3   Pondtail
4   Eelmoor Flash
4a Eelmoor Marsh
5   Claycart Flash
6   Rushmoor Flash
7   Fleet Pond
8   Ancells Pond & Meadow
9   Hawley Lake
10 Bourley Ponds
11 Badshot Lea Lake
12 Hilland Lake & Spring Lakes

Legend
- Basingstoke Canal
- Ponds
- Heathland
- Fen, Mire, Reeds & Swamp
- Arable & Grassland in Rotation
- Grasslands
- Amenity Grassland, Parkland, Formal Gardens
- Woodland (various)
- Parkland, Scrub & Orchards
- Built up areas

© Crown Copyright 2002 HCC 076651
Reproduced from the Ordnance
Survey Map with the permission of
the Controller of Her Majesty's
Stationery Office.

NB. Over the course of the last 20 years, the habitat of this area has been altered in a number of places. Consequently, this map does not show the exact position at the present day; rather it paints a general picture for the canal's surrounds over the past two decades. For instance, the area to both north and south of the canal near the Surrey Border is now mostly urban, as is land adjoining the northern boundary of Fleet, whilst in some places permanent grassland has replaced land marked on the map as 'Arable and Grassland in Rotation'.

a waterway that must have been pristine dragonfly habitat. Victorian botanists had long known the Basingstoke Canal as a rich collecting ground for their herbaria but the first published reference to its dragonflies seems to be that by a contributor to *The Times* in January 1910 who waxed lyrical about the "troops of gem-like dragonflies" about the Basingstoke Navigation at Aldershot (quoted in Vine 1994). This would seem to give the first canal records for Banded Demoiselle and (noting that the heathers were in flower) Common Blue Damselfly.

"A few of the larger species sweep from the bank and circle in sunny clearings among the fir trees with an audible rustle of their wings, but they are far outnumbered by the smaller and more brilliant kinds that seldom travel far from the waterside. One beautiful species, with large wings blotched with deep blue, seems perpetually drifting from one green sedge stem to another, and never leaves the shore. But flights of another and smaller kind, with a brilliant sky-blue body, wander at times some distance up the heathery slopes; and when a dozen or twenty of these brilliant little creatures leap suddenly into sparkling flight above the purple heather bloom it is a sight of fairy-like splendour".

The canal continued to decline. Most commercial barge traffic had ceased on the Hampshire parts by 1920 and navigation to Basingstoke became impossible after a roof-fall in the Greywell Tunnel in 1932. With only minimal maintenance the water way reverted to nature. Traffic ceased on the Surrey part in the 1940s and the canal was sold in 1949. The new owners failed to revive commercial trade and only carried out essential repairs, though some short stretches continued to be maintained for boat hire.

Naturalists had maintained a keen interest in the canal. A.W. Richards, a keen amateur entomologist who lived at Hawley, knew of 25 species of Odonata that could be collected along the Basingstoke Canal in the 1940s, though some of these would have bred in adjacent habitats. He seems to have mostly worked the stretch between Dogmersfield in Hampshire and Frimley Green in Surrey. Hairy Dragonfly, Downy Emerald and Brilliant Emerald were well-known to him as canal specialities by 1940 (Richards, 1941). Records of Odonata and aquatic plants for this period suggest strongly that although the canal was deteriorating as a navigation, the wildlife was thriving. Indeed, in 1947 a Government White Paper on the subject of nature conservation proposed the acquisition of 73 sites in Britain as national nature reserves, which include two parts of the Basingstoke Canal. Among the reasons cited was the canal's "great importance … for insects with aquatic larvae" (Byfield, 1990), presumably a reference to dragonflies. With the formation of the Nature Conservancy in 1949 the canal received early consideration to be one of the first SSSIs to be declared in Britain. The canal from Broad Oak to Crookham Village in Hampshire, together with two lengths in Surrey, were duly notified as SSSIs in 1955.

With no commercial barge traffic and only a small income from other sources, the canal was in a poor state of repair by 1960. Some parts in Surrey suffered a total loss of water but the Hampshire length fared better thanks to springs in the canal bed at Greywell. The future of the canal became the subject of much debate in the 1960s, the eventual outcome of which was the purchase by Hampshire and Surrey County Councils of the waterway from Greywell to the junction with the Wey Navigation. By this time the canal west of Greywell had mostly been sold off to farmers and property developers and what remained was derelict. The main interest of the County Councils was to create a recreational facility for the rapidly growing towns that bordered the canal, an objective that had been energetically promoted by canal enthusiasts who wished to see the canal restored for navigation. Restoration began at Winchfield in Hampshire in November 1973, initially by clearing the overgrown towpath and repairs to make canal structures safe. Dredging began at Colt Hill, Odiham, in 1975.

By the mid-1970s the wildlife interest of the canal was known to extend well beyond the SSSI. Restoration had been cautiously welcomed by naturalists but the impacts of dredging and motorised craft on canal ecology were especially controversial. Wildlife legislation did not give the then Nature Conservancy Council strong powers to protect SSSIs and, with no prospect of an acceptable compromise, the NCC reluctantly denotified the Hampshire SSSI in 1978. Two smaller SSSIs were declared to protect the chalk-stream flora at Greywell and a short stretch of more acidic water centred on Eelmoor Flash at Farnborough. Surveys had shown this to support an exceptional assemblage of dragonflies (Goodyear, 1977). The County Council agreed to dredge this section sympathetically.

The Wildlife and Countryside Act of 1981 gave more protection to SSSIs and the NCC better powers to protect them. The growing interest in wildlife conservation in Britain rekindled the debate about such conservation on the canal and led NCC to commission the first systematic botanical survey of the entire canal, covering Hampshire in 1986 and Surrey in 1987. The results showed the canal to support a greater number of wetland plants than any other canal, river, pond or lake in Great Britain (Hall, 1988). Because dredging had been carried out a section at a time spread over more than ten years, the aquatic flora quickly recolonised from seeds and the natural dispersal of plant fragments. Similarly, dragonflies continued to be present in excellent numbers, with 24 species recorded in the mid-1980s (Oates, 1986). The profile of wildlife was raised still further when the Greywell Tunnel was designated an SSSI on account of the large assemblage of bats using it as a winter roost (Stebbings, 1993).

However, the increasing recreational use of the canal continued to be cause for concern amongst naturalists, in particular the use of motorised boats of all kinds. There was a widely held belief that boat traffic was responsible for the decline in wildlife on other canals, a view supported by scientific research at the University of Liverpool which had demonstrated a decline in biodiversity once a threshold of boat traffic is exceeded (Byfield, 1990). These fears were reinforced by an entomological survey of the canal for Hampshire County Council which suggested seven species of dragonfly may have gone into decline (Oates, 1990). These concerns prompted local members of the British Dragonfly Society to set up a monitoring scheme in 1989, focused initially on the canal at Farnborough but later extended (Mundell, 1992).

The wealth of new survey information led the NCC to conclude much of the canal, including the entire length in Hampshire east of the Greywell Tunnel, met its criteria for SSSI notification and this was confirmed in 1994 after discussions with all interested parties. The reasons for notification describe the canal as an important for Odonata where 24 species had been recorded during 1992 and 1993. There was evidence for breeding for 19 of these. With the creation of a Basingstoke Canal Authority to manage the canal in 1990 and the adoption of a management plan that takes account of the needs to balance the requirements of recreation and conservation (Eaton, 1994), there should be grounds for optimism that a rich and diverse flora and fauna will remain one of canal's attractions. However, many naturalists remain concerned that wildlife on the canal, including dragonflies, has been in decline during the 1990s, especially on the Hampshire part.

Recording of Odonata has continued in every summer since 1989 in the form of counts of adults as seen from the towpath. Although many records are for the Pondtail to Aldershot section, all parts of the canal have been visited in at least some years. A total of 28 species has been seen over the canal during that period (including the Surrey part), though only 22 species are now recorded annually (Hall, 2001). There follows a description of the canal and the species likely to be encountered. For information about Odonata in the Surrey section, see Follett 1996.

The official long distance footpath beside the canal begins at Penny Bridge on the Greywell Road between Mapledurwell and Up Nately, at SU695521. Note there is not, at the time of writing in 2003, a car park at this location. The canal from here to the western portal of the Greywell Tunnel in Butter Wood was cleared of trees and dredged in 1992–93 but of late only the footpath has been maintained. This is a rural stretch of canal, frequently tree-lined, and is the only section in Hampshire excluded from the SSSI. Odonata were quick to colonise and 17 species have been recorded since 1993, though only 11 of these are seen regularly, including a population of Ruddy Darters. The ancient woodland of Butter Wood has considerable wildlife interest.

The canal in Hampshire has a number of car parks for visitors and these provide good starting points to observe dragonflies and other wildlife. Canal car parks are situated at Colt Hill (Odiham), Barley Mow Bridge (Winchfield), Chequers Wharf (Crookham Village), Reading Road (Fleet) and beside the A325 Farnborough Road. Other car parks exist near Claycart Bridge (Farnborough) and at Ash Lock (Aldershot). The last three are the best sites for visitors wishing to see the most species of Odonata, including those that are nationally or regionally uncommon. There is a small, unofficial parking area at Eelmoor Bridge.

At Greywell the canal is a classic chalk stream with beautifully clear water and luxuriant vegetation, though some parts are quite heavily shaded by bankside vegetation. This is the only section closed to boats of all kinds. Dragonfly numbers are not usually high here though most of the commoner species are present. From the aqueduct over the River Whitewater beside the ruin of Odiham Castle onwards the canal is open to navigation but traffic is generally low between there and Odiham. This is mostly an open stretch of canal bordered by fields, apart from a short stretch of gardens at North Warnborough. The margins are dominated by tall herbs or emergent swamp, but there are ample viewpoints over the open water too. Slightly more species are regularly seen here, including Banded Demoiselle and moderate numbers of Red-eyed Damselfly, whilst the blue damselflies are present in hundreds. Aquatic vegetation is abundant, but the calcareous water limits the number of species attracted to this part of the canal.

In the vicinity of Colt Hill the quality of the aquatic habitat deteriorates very markedly. The water is turbid, the abundance of aquatic vegetation is much less, especially in summer, and bankside vegetation is reduced to scattered clumps. The area is popular for anglers and for boating, but can no longer be recommended for those who prefer a quiet afternoon observing wildlife. East of Odiham the canal passes through a number of woodlands together with shorter stretches of open fields. Dragonfly numbers are poor with only the commoner species usually present. During 12 years, only 16 species have been recorded between Odiham and Bouley Mow Wharf, but only eight to ten of these are usually present, including Banded Demoiselle, Red-eyed Damselfly and

(ABOVE) Woolmer Pond, the shallowest of a series of lakes on the Longmoor Ranges, is subject to great fluctuations in water level but supports a good range of species. (BELOW) Warren Heath, Top Pond, at Hartley Wintney, one of a series of three ponds that support healthy populations of species such as Emerald Damselfly, Downy Emerald, and Black Darter © *Steve Cham*.

Two pictures showing habitat along the Basingstoke Canal. (ABOVE) Eelmoor Flash, one of the most important sites in Hampshire and (BELOW) the canal at Dogmersfield showing emergent vegetation and bordering trees that are so typical of the area. © *Bob Gibbons*.

(ABOVE) **Prime coastal dragonfly habitat at Titchfield Haven where Hairy Dragonflies are established** © *Titchfield Haven Reserve.* (BELOW) **Kingsley Pond, which along with Shortheath Pond is a man-made water on Wealden rocks of eastern Hampshire supporting healthy Odonata populations** © *John Taverner.*

Two small man-made waters on the high chalk. The National Trust recreation of a dew-pond on the top of Stockbridge Down (ABOVE), and an old garden swimming pool (BELOW) that was turned into a wildlife pond by the owners. Such small pools hold important Odonata populations. © *John Taverner*.

Migrant Hawker. The adjacent sites of Wilk's Water, Dogmersfield Lake and Tundry Pond are better dragonfly habitats and it is probable that a proportion of the insects seen over the canal are dispersing from these ponds.

It is the waterway from the Coxmoor Wood area through to Aldershot that has earned the canal its reputation as a site of importance for dragonflies in Hampshire. By now the water is less strongly alkaline and recreational use is less intensive. Though the ancient woodland of Coxmoor lines both banks, the Canal Authority has thinned trees on the south bank and the waterway here is sunny but sheltered. Aquatic, emergent and bankside vegetation is well established, providing opportunities to see unusual wild flowers, butterflies and hoverflies as well as dragonflies. It is here that Common Blue Damselflies, Azure Damselflies and Red-eyed Damselflies will be seen in their hundreds, whilst Brown Hawkers and Migrant Hawkers are often seen in double figures. The first of the canal's specialities, Brilliant Emerald, has been seen fairly frequently at Coxmoor during the 1990s. The canal through Crookham Village similarly has good numbers of damselflies and the commoner dragonflies, but much of it is very open and unshaded. The only place where Brilliant Emerald and Downy Emerald may be glimpsed is at Zebon Copse. It was at the adjacent Zephon Common where the canal first entered an area of heathland vegetation and peat cuts. This is mostly overgrown now, though Hampshire County Council have begun managing one part as a nature reserve and have opened out an area of marsh.

Little diminishes natural biodiversity more greatly than urbanisation. The great heath of Crookham Common has become the modern town of Fleet and Church Crookham, extending from the edge of Zebon Copse through to Pondtail Bridge and caging the canal in housing estates. Urban planning dictates that trees are preserved on the canal banks, thus condemning much of the canal to semi-shade, in addition to the pollution and disturbance that characterise an urban environment. Though much of the canal is lined by tall emergent swamp, there are few submerged plants. The dragonfly fauna is correspondingly poor with only eight species seen regularly, though in low numbers.

In contrast, east of Fleet there are recent records of 23 species, including both Brilliant Emerald and Downy Emerald. There have also been occasional sightings of the other Basingstoke Canal speciality, the Hairy Dragonfly. The canal here passes through heathland. Indeed, the heathland between the canal and the A323 has been included within the Basingstoke Canal SSSI because of its value as a hinterland over which Odonata may disperse and because of a breeding population of Keeled Skimmers in the bog pools. The heath north of the canal, currently being brought into sympathetic management for conservation, has provided records of White-legged Damselfly, which is occasionally recorded by the canal here. Populations of many of the commoner species are strong in this section, though several of the 23 species have been recorded only rarely and cannot be considered resident.

The next block of open heathland is at Eelmoor Marsh SSSI which, together with the grasslands of Farnborough airfield and army training areas south of the canal, provide a canal hinterland of considerable extent. Eelmoor Marsh is an important dragonfly site in its own right, but lies immediately adjacent to the canal and close to the equally important site of Eelmoor Flash. When taken together, these Eelmoor habitats have combined records of 27 species. With its combination of wooded stretches, canalside heathlands and the three canalside flashes at Eelmoor, Claycart and Rushmoor, plus a recently restored smaller flash at Claycart Hill, this section is the best part of the canal in Hampshire for dragonflies. This is the stronghold of Hairy Dragonfly, Brilliant Emerald and Downy Emerald, and almost the full suite of other species known from the canal, including Common Hawker and Ruddy Darter. Occasional specimens of Small Red Damselfly, Golden-ringed Dragonfly and Keeled Skimmer may also be seen, though these stray from the adjacent heathlands. Black Darters, which formerly were seen fairly frequently over the canal, were last recorded at Eelmoor Flash in 1986, though they are still breeding on adjacent heathland.

The urban influence of Aldershot, together with some wooded sections, may account for the fewer species recorded east of Rushmoor Flash, but the well-vegetated and relatively less used canal between Queen's Avenue and Ash Lock may nonetheless provide sightings of most species present at Eelmoor and Claycart. Beyond Ash Lock the canal crosses the River Blackwater on a raised embankment where it is luxuriant with both submerged and emergent vegetation. There are records of 21 species, including four-figure counts of some of the commoner damselflies and a few tantalising records of the Variable Damselfly, the only recent reports from anywhere along the canal in either county. Below the embankment lies Lakeside Park Local Nature Reserve and, in both directions, the corridor of the River Blackwater where over 30 lakes and ponds have been created in former gravel workings, a wetland complex with recent records of 26 species.

There is no doubt the canal has changed as a habitat since the 1960s. Then, in an unmaintained condition it had silted up, becoming in effect a shallow, linear pond stretching from Greywell to Aldershot and linking many rich wildlife sites. Some of these have since been lost to urban spread, drainage or other agricultural activities, though others are now actively and sympathetically managed as nature reserves. Contemporary accounts describe a canal with clear water rarely more than 0.6 metres deep, supporting abundant vegetation. The requirements of recreation are for a waterway dredged out to its full depth to permit navigation by motor cruisers and well stocked with fish to satisfy the many anglers who regularly fish its waters.

Meanwhile, chemicals wash into the canal from farmland, roads and gardens and unmanaged woodlands have been left to grow tall, casting shade across the water. In addition, the increasing urbanisation of the area, particularly from Fleet to the county boundary, brings the familiar problems of fly-tipping, pollution and the thoughtless dumping of alien species into the canal. There is now a serious infestation of the severely invasive New Zealand Pigmyweed, presumably discarded from garden ponds, and unknown numbers of North American crayfish and terrapins. With so many stresses on the ecosystem, it is inevitable that numbers of many dragonfly species have declined since the halcyon days of the 1970s and one species, the Black Darter, seems to be extinct as a canal species.

With ever increasing demands for leisure facilities of the kind promoted on the canal, there can never be a return to those days of uncountable numbers of Odonata, but conservationists should work to ensure that the canal is managed to preserve remaining dragonfly habitats. The three flashes at Farnborough are managed as off-channel nature reserves by the Hampshire and Isle of Wight Wildlife Trust. Opportunities to create more habitat, such as the recent restoration of the small flash at Claycart Hill by the Canal Authority, are welcome indeed. Some people have said that a canal without boats is a dead canal. Fortunately, there are many who feel the same about a canal without dragonflies.

Figure 7. The habitat of the Needs Ore Point Nature Reserve
Map produced by HBIC with special thanks to Purgle Linham and Nicky Court

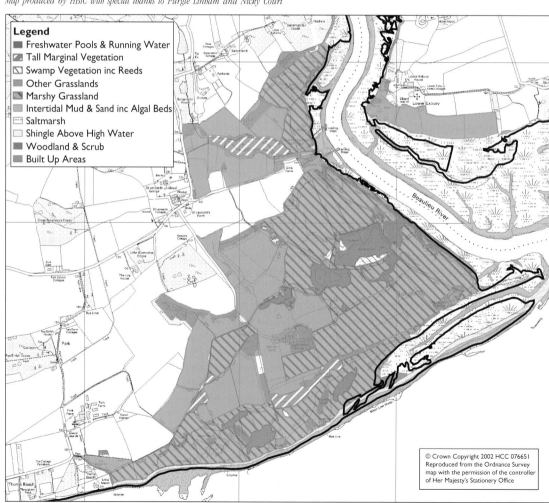

Legend
- Freshwater Pools & Running Water
- Tall Marginal Vegetation
- Swamp Vegetation inc Reeds
- Other Grasslands
- Marshy Grassland
- Intertidal Mud & Sand inc Algal Beds
- Saltmarsh
- Shingle Above High Water
- Woodland & Scrub
- Built Up Areas

© Crown Copyright 2002 HCC 076651
Reproduced from the Ordnance Survey map with the permission of the controller of Her Majesty's Stationery Office

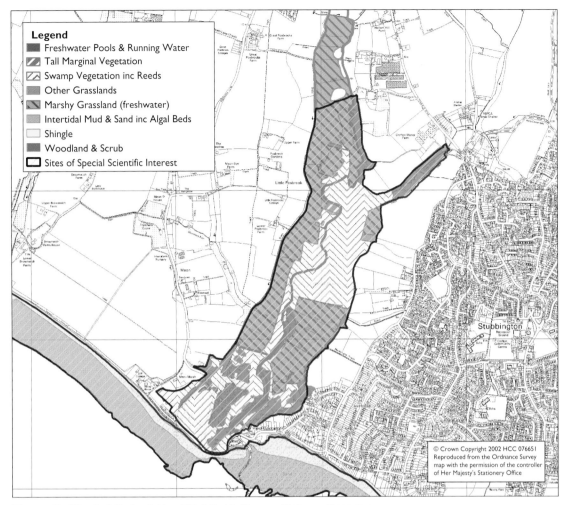

Legend
- ■ Freshwater Pools & Running Water
- ▨ Tall Marginal Vegetation
- ▨ Swamp Vegetation inc Reeds
- ■ Other Grasslands
- ◪ Marshy Grassland (freshwater)
- ■ Intertidal Mud & Sand inc Algal Beds
- □ Shingle
- ■ Woodland & Scrub
- ▭ Sites of Special Scientific Interest

© Crown Copyright 2002 HCC 076651
Reproduced from the Ordnance Survey
map with the permission of the controller
of Her Majesty's Stationery Office

Figure 8. The habitat of the Titchfield Haven Nature Reserve
Map produced by HBIC with special thanks to Purgle Linham and Nicky Court

THE COASTAL STRETCH From Hurst shingle spit in the west to the county boundary in the east, much of the Hampshire coast is low-lying. Indeed, considerable stretches are below high-water mark and only form dry land because sea-walls have been built to keep the Solent at bay. The result is a series of coastal marshes and meadows that are drained by a network of small ditches, with a number of brackish pools of varying sizes. This reclamation has resulted in a wetland complex that forms a dragonfly habitat of considerable importance. Furthermore, much of this land lies in nature reserves run by Hampshire County Council, English Nature and the Hampshire and Isle of Wight Wildlife Trust so that habitat is managed with wildlife in mind.

One species that has recently taken advantage of such habitat is the Hairy Dragonfly. In the ditches that surround Blackwater, a man-made pool behind Needs Ore Point whose origins probably stretch back to the times of the monks at Beaulieu Abbey, the Hairy Dragonfly can be found in some strength, especially along the main drainage ditch that skirts the southern boundary of Blackwater. Half a dozen or so males have been seen patrolling this rather short stretch of ditch in recent years, whilst tandem pairs and ovipositing females are evidence that the species has truly colonised this area.

A similar situation is found in the water complex at Titchfield Haven. Like Needs Ore, it would seem that the Hairy Dragonfly's colonisation of the area is a relatively recent event, not perhaps surprising in view of the general spread in the species' range in southern England. These two sites are perhaps the stronghold of the Hairy Dragonfly along the Hampshire coast and it is possible that the species has spread from Needs Ore and Titchfield Haven to colonise nearby sites inland, and along the coast to Farlington Marshes where reedbed management north of the A27 has seen this species flourish.

The Nature Reserve at Titchfield Haven is certainly one of the most important Odonata sites along the Hampshire coast. The maze of ditches and small pools that have been created by Barry Duffin and his wildlife rangers has attracted 18 species to date and the habitat is kept in good order for these insects. Similarly, at Needs Ore the area around Blackwater is a major dragonfly site that supports a similar number of species to Titchfield Haven. These two areas, along with Old Bursldon Nature Haven, form the most important dragonfly sites along the Hampshire coast.

It is fortunate that, at Titchfield Haven, the best dragonfly habitat is found in the pools, ditches and canal rather than the main course of the River Meon, because in November 2003 a massive pollution took place in the river when thousands of gallons of raw sewage entered the river at Titchfield when a metre-wide pipe burst. Oxygen levels in the Meon below the leak dropped to around a third of their previous level and although teams from the Environment Agency worked day and night to pump oxygen into the river, there must have been some damage to Dragonfly larvae found in that stretch of water. Thanks to the Environment Agency, it is hoped that damage was kept to reasonable level, although the exact extent will not be known for at least a year.

Both dragonflies and damselflies have taken advantage of these coastal wetlands. With the smaller damselflies, the most widespread species are the Large Red Damselfly, the Azure Damselfly and the Blue-tailed Damselfly, all of which can be found in some numbers at several localities. Apart from the Hairy Dragonfly, the main species of Anisoptera are the Migrant Hawker, Southern Hawker, Emperor, Four-spotted Chaser, Broad-bodied Chaser and Common Darter.

THE WEALDEN ROCKS OF EAST HAMPSHIRE In the extreme east of Hampshire, a small section of the eroded Wealden anticline crosses the county boundary between Petersfield and Bentley, exposing the oldest rocks in Hampshire which in descending order from the surface are Upper Greensand, Gault Clay and Lower Greensand. Gault is a heavy, impervious clay so that it is crossed by a number of small streams, and a good deal of standing water is present at times of heavy rainfall, whereas much of the Upper Greensand allows water to pass through with some ease, depending on whether or not bands of clay are present. The Lower Greensands vary in their permeability.

This habitat does not provide dragonflies with conditions that begin to match that provided by the Tertiary rocks of both north and south Hampshire, but neither are they wholly unsuitable for these insects. Indeed, if one were to produce a typical distribution map for a Hampshire dragonfly, it would show a heavy concentration of records on the Tertiary rocks to the north and south of the chalk, a fair scatter of occurrences along the main chalk rivers and on the Wealden rocks, and a thin scattering over the chalk above the main river valleys.

The Upper and Lower Greensands, along with the Gault Clay, have not been covered in depth by odonatists and so the species' distribution maps may well underestimate the strength of some species in this geological area. More work is needed on this small part of Hampshire to discover the true situation.

THE CHALKLANDS It has already been stated that the great mass of Upper Chalk is mostly devoid of natural water supplies and in consequence does not offer much potential breeding habitat to dragonflies other than those waters created by man. However, the whole of a dragonfly's life-cycle is not spent by water, which is only vital for their reproductive activities.

There are a number of reasons why these insects leave water and at such times they may be found in dry environments. Some are migrants and their journeys take them into unexpected types of country. Sub-adults leave water for a few days until their wings harden for efficient flight, and after emerging, the immature insects will move away from water whilst this process takes place. Furthermore, if sub-adults insects with their weaker powers of flight stay in the open near water, they may be harassed by males searching for mates or killed by predators who find capture easy at this stage. Having mated and laid, females will leave water for a while until they are ready to mate again, whilst in poor weather, even adult males will desert their pools and hang up perhaps at some distance from water or hunt along open rides in woodland. Even in fine weather, there are a few favoured spots where fully adult males can be found well away from even the smallest pond. For these and other reasons, individual dragonflies are found on the chalk and some sizeable breeding colonies exist in both natural and man-made waters.

A few examples will suffice to demonstrate this point, all taken from the high chalk around Winchester. A female Golden-ringed Dragonfly was found eating a large Bumble Bee beside a hedge on dry chalk farmland and a male of the same species was seen hunting a woodland ride in dull weather, both far from any suitable breeding water, whilst on two occasions another male was seen in a garden high on the chalk where there was a very small pond. A female Broad-bodied Chaser was discovered sitting on top of a Hawthorn hedge and another female of that species was seen resting on Bramble, again far removed from water areas of any size. Male Southern Hawkers have been seen not infrequently on the chalk, sometimes hunting in woodland, sometimes hung up in the early morning or in overcast weather, and sometimes hunting urban gardens. Common Darters of both sexes have been seen frequently resting in woodland or suburban gardens. Indeed, several Hampshire species are likely to occur on dry chalk country, far from the nearest suitable breeding grounds other than garden ponds.

Crab Wood, close to Winchester, is a locality where male Southern Hawkers are often seen hunting and at this locality it is clear that we still have much to learn about the fine detail of dragonfly habitat. In that wood, there is one particular ride that to all intents and purposes is just like the other rides in the wood, lined mostly with Oaks and Hazel with a dense undergrowth of Dog's Mercury, Bracken, thistles and other plants, yet it regularly holds the odd fully adult male Southern Hawker, hunting between the trees in both dull and sunny weather, whereas the other rides are seldom used by the species.

However, the supply of man-made ponds on the chalk is now an important habitat for dragonflies. Large dragonflies will breed in pools of very modest size; Southern Hawkers have been found emerging from garden pools no more than three metres in length. Just how important a habitat these man-made pools have become is not known as no survey of garden and ornamental ponds in the county has been made. From what limited data we do possess, it is clear that man-made ponds, whether they be in gardens, garden centres, parks or other situations, already support a considerable number of dragonflies and the previous text has stated that this supply of water is likely to increase in the future. The importance to dragonflies of garden ponds on the chalk is a subject that would repay investigation.

So, the dry chalk is not quite the dragonfly desert that one may suppose it to be; it is studded with oases that we have created and even its waterless parts may be visited by dragonflies that for various reasons have removed themselves from water. In this respect, the maps for each individual species underestimate the value of the chalk to dragonflies, because few people bother to report the odd insect seen here and few odonatists make special sorties to the chalk to look for these insects.

PART FOUR

SYSTEMATIC LIST OF SPECIES

When the text refers to the strength of a species, numbers will obviously be different according to the species in question. Dragonflies are predators, and it is a widespread rule in nature that large predators, being in the top part of a food chain, are less numerous than smaller predators. What constitutes a strong population for the Emperor Dragonfly would be weak for most damselflies. So, whereas a half a dozen male Emperor Dragonflies on a pond complex will represent a strong population, it may take a hundred or more Azure Damselflies in that area to qualify for the same description. Furthermore, some species occur in larger and denser communities than others; in Hampshire, one would not expect to find Red-eyed Damselfly numbers equal to those of Azure Damselflies at those species' best localities, nor Brown Hawkers in the sort of numbers that may be found with Migrant or Southern Hawkers. The *Distribution maps* for species reflect the difference in numbers. **Maps** for the damselfly species and for the Darters and Skimmers are divided into **four** categories of adult numbers, the four groups being: 1; 2–5; 6–20; >20. Maps for most of the largest dragonflies are divided into **three** categories: 1; 2–5; >5. A key to the symbols is provided with each map. The division into two separate groupings is because the larger dragonflies do not commonly produce counts of over 20 individuals at a site at the same time, whereas with the damselflies, and dragonflies such as the Common Darter, counts may often reach three figures.

These numbers do not, of course, represent the entire population of an area; rather they show the maximum estimate of numbers that have been seen at any **one** time. The number of adult dragonflies seen at any one time at the breeding site is just a fraction of the whole population. Many species time-share at a site with territorial males spending varying times at a pool before leaving to go off to feed. As one leaves to feed, it leaves the water available for another male to fly in and take its place. For a fuller account of this behaviour in the Downy Emerald, see Brooks, McGeeney and Cham (1997). A water complex might hold half a dozen Emperors at one moment, but they are simply the ones in view. There will be others based on that complex that were either feeding elsewhere at the time of the count, were still to hatch, or had already died. For some species with a very limited distribution in Hampshire, such as the Southern Damselfly, a more detailed map shows where the species occurs.

The maps give a good idea of a species' general distribution in Hampshire. Figure 9a shows the number of species in each ten-kilometre square in Britain. Not surprisingly, dragonfly mapping in Hampshire has been rather thin on the chalklands as they are less attractive to dragonfly recorders. Work has concentrated on the north and south of the county where the underlying geology has resulted in habitats that are more suited to Odonata. The distribution maps in this section of the book consequently underestimate the distribution of most species on the chalk, as the previous text has shown that man-made ponds and pools on the chalk now provide a not inconsiderable habitat that has been discovered by our more common and numerous species. Much work remains to be undertaken on this under-recorded area; it is very probable that almost every one-kilometre square on the chalk has seen at least one species of dragonfly in the past 15 years.

Dragonflies are warmth-loving creatures, so the number of species tends to increase from north to south in Britain. Being in the extreme south, with highly suitable habitat in the New Forest and similar Tertiary rocks in the north of the county, Hampshire can be counted amongst the best counties in the country for this order of insects, as Figure 9a shows.

However, when one looks at a more detailed map of Hampshire (Figure 9b), it can be seen that the distribution of species is far from even, as the previous text has shown. The central mass of chalk is largely bare of records, whilst Tertiary rocks in the north and the south, and to some extent the Secondary rocks in the east, hold the bulk of the records.

The species distribution maps show gaps for some species. In the New Forest, for instance, one might expect the Large Red Damselfly and Azure Damselfly in every kilometre square, but such is not the case. The mapping of Odonata in Hampshire is far from complete and this volume might encourage field workers to visit blank squares and try to fill in the gaps. This is the first book of its kind on the county's dragonflies and it is to be hoped that further fieldwork will add to the distribution maps published here.

Following on from the comments of the previous paragraph, the chalk appears to be a dragonfly desert on most of the maps, but this is not the case. Odonatists obviously concentrate on areas such as the New Forest or the Basingstoke Canal, as a visit to the chalk may well produce a complete blank away from ponds and streams. It is hoped that this pioneer book will encourage workers to search the squares that are blank on the maps to fill in the many gaps that exist.

If a species has Red Data Book status, is included in the 'Nationally Scarce' category, or is a UK or Hampshire BAP species, that status will appear after the species' name in the Systematic list (for explanations of those terms, see **Definitions** section at the beginning of this book).

For some species, there is a final sub-heading of **Additional Notes** or **Behaviour**. These occur where we think that the Hampshire records might add fresh information of importance for those species generally, and would be of interest for areas other than Hampshire. An obvious example is the Southern Damselfly where recent research has led to discoveries that would apply to other sites where the species is found.

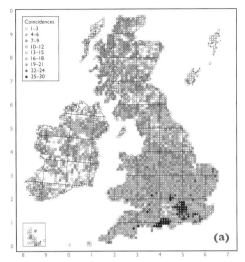

Figure 9. Coincidence maps showing the number of dragonfly species recorded (a) in each ten-kilometre square in Britain and (b) in each one-kilometre square in Hampshire

Maps produced by Steve Cham from the British Dragonfly Society Data-base

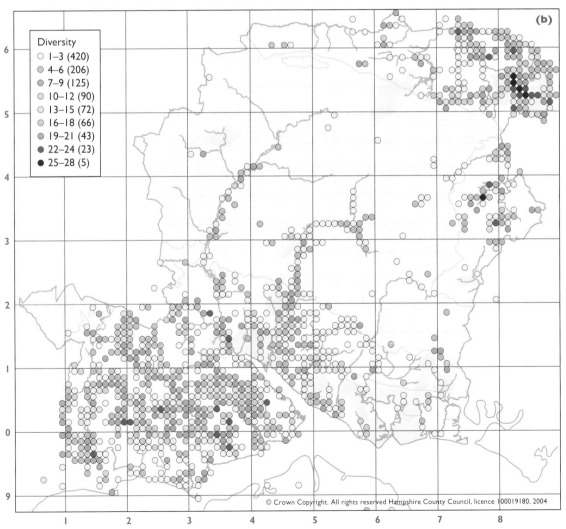

Damselflies *Zygoptera*

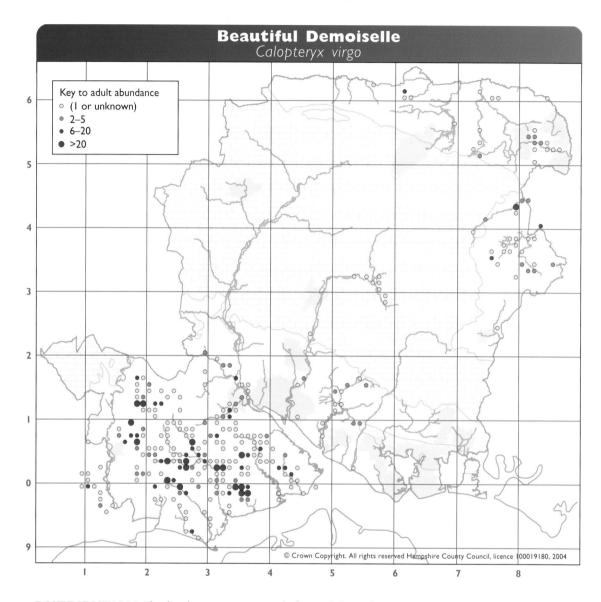

Beautiful Demoiselle
Calopteryx virgo

Key to adult abundance
○ (1 or unknown)
● 2–5
● 6–20
● >20

DISTRIBUTION The distribution map is typical of several dragonfly species in Hampshire, showing as it does a heavy concentration on the southern Tertiary rocks, especially in the New Forest, a reasonable presence in the north-east of the county and a complete absence from the chalk. It is interesting to compare this map with that of the closely-related Banded Demoiselle (see page 40), where rivers and the Basingstoke Canal dominate.

HABITAT This is a species of small, clear streams with gravel beds such as are found in the New Forest, usually with well-vegetated banks. Both sexes use overhanging branches and bushes, such as Alder and Bog-myrtle, as perches. The previous paragraph referred to the difference in the distributions of the Beautiful and Banded Demoiselles; a key factor would seem to be the nature of the stream bed, the present species preferring gravel and the Banded Demoiselle silt. In the New Forest, females oviposit into aquatic vegetation, especially patches of Common Water-crowfoot, females ovipositing alone submerging below the water surface.

MAJOR LOCALITIES So many of the gravel streams in the New Forest have strong populations that it is perhaps misleading to pick out a few as major localities, but examples may be given such as Crockford Stream, Ober Water and Latchmore Brook. The main sites for this species within Hampshire are to be found in the New Forest and some its neighbouring land, and the similar Tertiary rocks in the north-east of the county. Most of the streams within the New Forest that are not too shaded by trees will hold good populations.

POPULATION STRENGTHS Populations will vary from year to year, as with most species, but favoured areas can produce 50+ per 100 m of stream in good years. An exceptionally high count of over 100 individuals was recorded at Latchmore Bottom on 21st July 1996, whilst records of over 20 individuals have been recorded for the River Wey at Bentley on 28th June 1991 and at Upper Crockford on both 26th June 1995 and dates in the early 2000s.

FLIGHT PERIOD In some years this species can be found in early May, but more commonly the first fly in the third week of that month. It can then be seen through to the end of August or even in early September, with a peak during June and early July.

EARLIEST/LATEST DATES The earliest records for this species are both from Peaked Hill in the New Forest on 6th May 1990 and 2003, whilst the latest is at Ober Water on 24th September 1990.

Male in New Forest stream © *Barry Hilling*

BEHAVIOUR Males will vigorously defend a short stretch of bankside. When numbers are high this leads to regular clashes between males as the two spiral in an aerial display as one tries to displace the other. Females are attracted to streams where submerged aquatic vegetation predominates and along the New Forest streams, patches of Common Water-crowfoot are favoured areas. Following mating, the female oviposits alone with the male often on guard nearby. Sometimes more than one female will oviposit in the same small patch. They often submerge completely, continuing their task under water, thus ensuring that all parts of the plant are utilised.

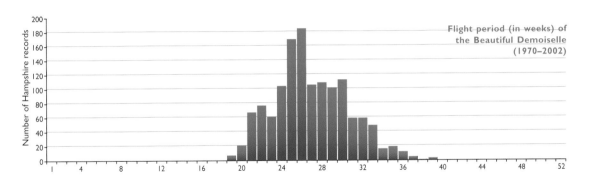

Flight period (in weeks) of
the Beautiful Demoiselle
(1970–2002)

Number of Hampshire records (y-axis)

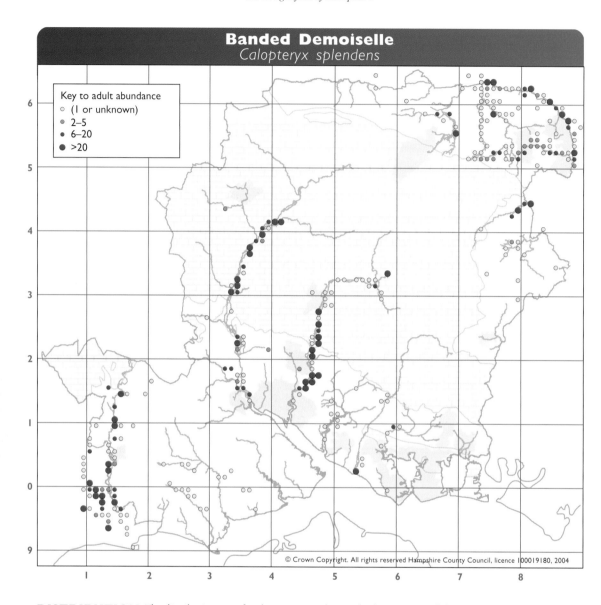

Banded Demoiselle
Calopteryx splendens

Key to adult abundance
○ (1 or unknown)
● 2–5
● 6–20
● >20

DISTRIBUTION The distribution map for this species picks out the larger rivers of the county and various stations along the Basingstoke Canal. Otherwise, there is a scatter of records from other parts of the county so that this species is found in all of Hampshire's geological types where suitable habitat occurs. The map shows an interesting comparison between the habitat preferences of this species and the closely-related Beautiful Demoiselle, especially along the valleys of the Test and Itchen where the Beautiful Demoiselle is absent.

HABITAT The preferred habitat is a slow-flowing stream or river with a bed of soft silt. Typical of this is the River Test immediately below Stockbridge where the river flows through water meadows with public access, the Demoiselles being found mainly where the river's bank is lined with quite dense, metre-high vegetation. Where the banks are bare of such vegetation, the insects are absent. A little upstream from this spot is another regular site where a tiny bay in the Test's bank, with a dense mass of reeds, harbours a small population, the species again being mostly absent from nearby stretches where the larvae would perhaps be in danger from the speed of the river's flow. This is in sharp contrast to the previous species, the Banded Demoiselle being absent from most New Forest streams with their beds of stones and sand. A glance at the coincidence map shows the distribution of the two species in Hampshire's one-kilometre squares (see page 38) and immediately highlights the differences in the distribution of the two species.

MAJOR LOCALITIES The chalk rivers and streams of Hampshire are amongst the main places where this species is to be found. The River Test, with its many carriers and streams around the Stockbridge area, has many favoured sites. The Itchen Valley Country Park and the Winchester Water-meadows are amongst the better locations on the River Itchen, whilst in the west of the area, the River Avon has a number of places where the species is well represented. The River Meon, from Titchfield Haven to East Meon village is another stronghold. In the north of the county, the River Wey and other streams also hold good populations. In the Blackwater Valley, the species is found at a number of sites (e.g. Moor Green, Ash, Broadwater and Shepherd Meadows).

POPULATION STRENGTHS It is not unusual to find in excess of 50 adults along stretches of river where this species is to be found. Three-figure counts have been made in peak season at localities such as Itchen Valley Country Park on 7th June 1993 and on the River Wey near Bentley on 25th June 1992. A number of three-figure counts have also come from the River Blackwater, with 385 there at Hawley on 29th July 2000, and similar counts could probably be made along other rivers such as the Loddon. Most of these high counts are just over the border into Surrey, some of the waters in that area spanning both counties and the Hampshire population must be considerable.

Male covered in early morning dew © *Peter Allen*

FLIGHT PERIOD Adults of this species are on the wing a little later than the previous species, their flying season starting in early May and extending to the middle of September.

EARLIEST/LATEST DATES The Basingstoke Canal at Ash provides the earliest record, on 15th May 1994, with the latest also on the Basingstoke Canal, near Odiham, on 15th September 1997.

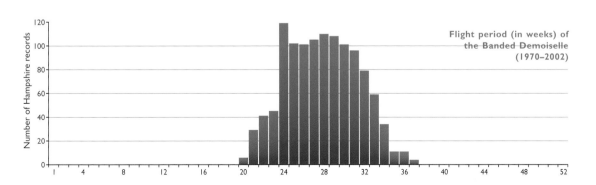

Flight period (in weeks) of the Banded Demoiselle (1970–2002)

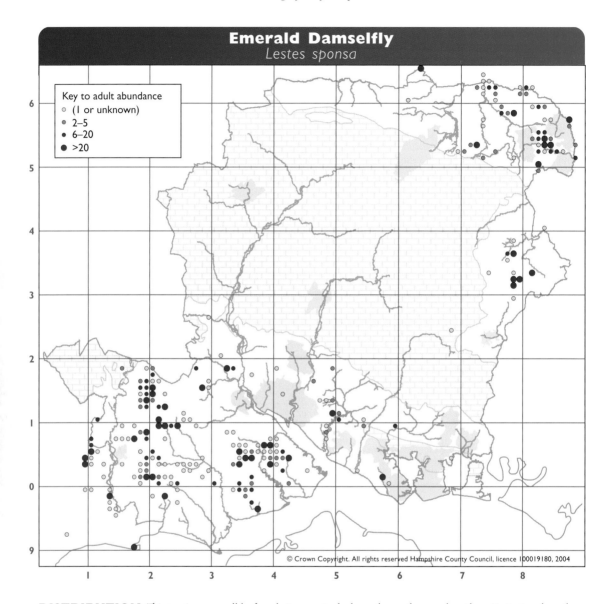

Emerald Damselfly
Lestes sponsa

Key to adult abundance
- ○ (1 or unknown)
- ◔ 2–5
- ◑ 6–20
- ● >20

DISTRIBUTION This species may well be found at any water body on the southern and northern Tertiaries where there is shallow water with a well-vegetated margin. Several of the ponds and flushes in and around the New Forest maintain good numbers with similar populations at Bramshill Plantation and the River Blackwater complex. However, it appears to have died out on the Basingstoke Canal, where it was common in the more distant past, but by the 1990s it had become very local and seen only in low numbers. It is now well established at Eelmoor Marsh, beside the canal, but is somewhat localised over the whole canal area (Hall, 2000). In that area the species is widespread, occurring at suitable heathland ponds and pools throughout the heathlands of North East Hampshire (e.g. Bramshill Plantation, Yateley Common and Bourley Ponds). A further population exists on the rocks of the Wealden anticline and a large population can be found on Ministry of Defence land at Woolmer Forest.

HABITAT The Emerald Damselfly occurs in a wide variety of still water habitats, the common factors usually being shallow water and dense emergent vegetation, although populations do occur at the margins of deep ponds and along slow moving water bodies (e.g. Burley Railway). It is also recorded breeding in atypical habitats, such as Broomy Pond in the New Forest where the edges are steep and the water relatively deep (*ca.* 1 metre). The dense vegetation is a requirement for oviposition; after selecting a stem, the female begins inserting ova above water level and works her way down until she is sometimes completely submerged. Both males and females perch at right angles to the vegetation. The species readily colonises newly created shallow pools on heathland; such pool creation at Eelmoor Marsh was quickly followed by an expansion in range and numbers. It is also found at seasonal pools around the army training area of Long Valley near Aldershot.

MAJOR LOCALITIES In and around the New Forest, the species is well represented at Broomy Pond, Burley Railway, East End Gravel Pit, Holbury Mill Pond, Long Pond South and Sable Waters. To the east of Southampton Water, Botley Wood has become a stronghold, whilst in north Hampshire Eelmoor Marsh is one of the main localities along with Ancell's Farm, Yateley Country Park, Kingsley Pond, Shortheath Pond, Woolmer Pond and various sites on the Basingstoke Canal.

POPULATION STRENGTHS The largest populations have been recorded at several sites in and around the New Forest, with well over 100 individuals at Dibden Bottom on 26th August 1991, at Great Goswell Copse on 2nd August 1990, on a 200 m stretch of water at Burley Railway on a date that cannot be precisely traced, and at Sable Waters on 4th August 2003. At the last-named site, the count could well have been over 200. At Botley Wood on 15th July 2003, 200+ newly emerged Emerald Damselflies were flushed from around the edge of Toby's Pond. At Eelmoor Marsh, an exceptional count of 88 individuals and nine mating pairs was made on 16th July 2001 at Cody Pond. It is not uncommon to see 20 adults at many sites in both the north and south of the county.

Male at a New Forest pool © *Alan Hold*

FLIGHT PERIOD The species is normally first seen in mid-June with a flying season that lasts until the end of September with the odd record in October. It is most abundant in July, and records suggest that the flight period starts a week later in the north of the county compared with the south.

EARLIEST/LATEST DATES The earliest date for this species is 13th June 1992 at Broomy Pond, whilst the latest is the 8th October 2000 at Akercome Bottom.

BEHAVIOUR This species has an exceptionally rapid larval development. Ova laid in the previous summer over-winter in diapause and this suspended development results in a synchronised emergence, enabling the species to survive at shallow water sites that tend to dry out during the summer. As the water temperatures rise in spring, ova hatch and the larvae develop in a short period of time to start emergence during June.

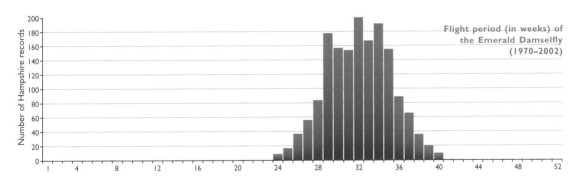

Flight period (in weeks) of
the Emerald Damselfly
(1970–2002)

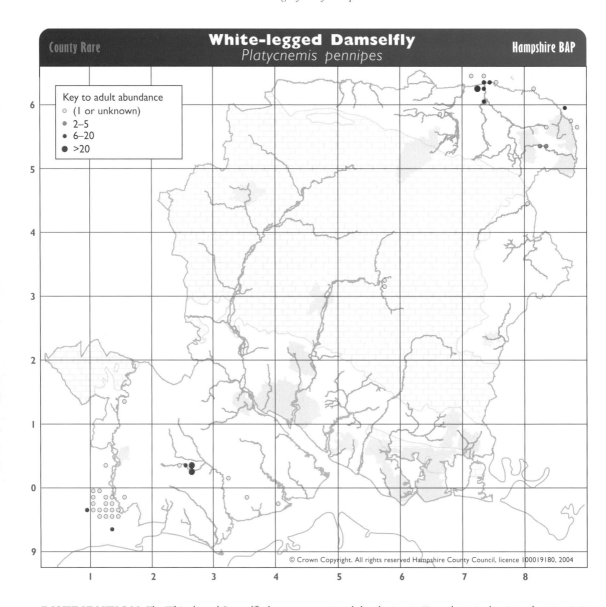

DISTRIBUTION The White-legged Damselfly has a very restricted distribution in Hampshire. At the time of writing it is limited to a few sites along rivers of North Hampshire and one short length of the Ober Water in the New Forest. On the latter it occurs just upstream from Puttles Bridge with over 90% of recent records coming from that area. The main stretch is surrounded by heathland, although in places tall bushes overhang the stream which is very shallow, very small and very slow-flowing. There would appear to be an abundance of similar stretches of stream in the New Forest, although clearly the particular stretch used has qualities as yet unknown to us that other Forest streams do not possess. There are also isolated records on the Itchen that need further investigation.

The species was known to be common in the New Forest until the 1940s, along with the Club-tailed Dragonfly which was abundant on the Ober Water during the 1930s and 1940s, but declined dramatically during the 1950s to the point of local extinction. It is generally thought that the demise of the Club-tailed Dragonfly on the Ober Water was due to the removal of bankside vegetation by human interference and opening the river banks to livestock; such disturbance, if widespread through the New Forest, would also have led to a decline in White-legged Damselfly numbers, although one of the main Ober Water sites is by a ford where Forest animals regularly come to cross and drink and in so doing trample the bankside and floating vegetation to a considerable extent.

Immature female *lactea* phase © *Tony Welstead*

It was also reported to be common on parts of the Avonwater in the 1940s (Fraser 1950) and occurred around the confluence of the Moors River and the South Moors River around the same time. Records supplied by the Dorset Environmental Records Centre suggest that the species has undergone a major decline in the Moors River and those stretches of the River Stour in vice-county 11. A few are still recorded at Town Common, Christchurch, but this situation warrants further monitoring.

A strong population formerly existed near the eastern end of the Basingstoke Canal in Surrey, but this died out in the 1960s as that part of the canal became derelict. There were no records from the Hampshire part of the canal until 1986, when one was seen at Ash Embankment on the county border. In the same summer there were several records close to the River Blackwater. Searches initiated by these records eventually led to the discovery in 1991 of a small colony near to the confluence of the Blackwater and Whitewater Rivers at Wheeler's Farm near Bramshill. The river here is the county boundary with Berkshire. The Environment Agency has subsequently recorded larvae on 20 dates in the period 1991 to 2000, especially from the River Whitewater near Heckfield Place and the River Loddon. Individuals recorded in the recent past at Wellington Country Park may have wandered from the nearby river.

The situation on the Basingstoke Canal is more enigmatic, but records are becoming more frequent. There were single records in 1993 and 1998, both to the east of Fleet at Norris Hill. In the period 2000 to 2003 there were nine more records, at Lousey Moor (north east of Odiham) in 2000, Coxmoor in 2001 and 2003, Pondtail Heath in 2000 and 2002 and at Eelmoor in 2000 and 2002. The best year was 2000, when one or two were seen close to the canal at Eelmoor on three dates in June and July, including an immature female (f. *lactea*) on 16th June. Eight were disturbed from vegetation on Pondtail Heath adjacent to the canal and a ninth was seen on the canal margin. Most of these damselflies were disturbed from rank grass or heathland near the canal.

In that part of vice-county 11 which is now in Dorset, but covered by this volume for reasons given in the previous text, the species was also recorded on the River Stour (Prendergast, 1991).

Adult male resting by the Ober Water © *John Taverner*

HABITAT The species generally favours larger streams and rivers with slow-flowing water, luxuriant bankside vegetation and surrounding meadows, and according to the *Atlas of the Dragonflies of Britain and Ireland* (Merritt, Moore and Eversham 1996), along unshaded sections of these. Several areas of its haunt on the Ober Water are shaded however, and the stream in question is very small with a gravel bed, so the Ober Water site is somewhat of an enigma in terms of habitat. Nationally, this species has made a dramatic recovery in other counties where it occurs and is expanding its range. As river management has become more sympathetic to the needs of conservation, bankside vegetation and adjacent meadows have been allowed to develop the luxuriant vegetation that the species favours. Large populations along the Thames are moving down tributaries such as the Loddon and it is very likely that this species will continue to expand along the Rivers Blackwater and Whitewater into new areas of north Hampshire.

It has been widely quoted that the species is susceptible to pollution, although there is very little evidence to support this view. Prendergast (1991) expresses the opinion that pollution cannot be the only reason for the limited distribution in Dorset, which is more likely to be the result of former riverbank management that was not sympathetic to the needs of dragonflies. From the 1940s to the 1970s, rivers underwent major bank clearances that led to significant population crashes amongst some dragonfly species and similar activities seem to have resulted in the loss of many New Forest sites. Recent work on the species has shown that the quality of bankside vegetation is a major factor determining where this species occurs (Cham, 2003).

Ample vegetation is needed because tandem pairs oviposit in floating stems and leaves of aquatic plants with females ovipositing by moving down into the water until fully submerged.

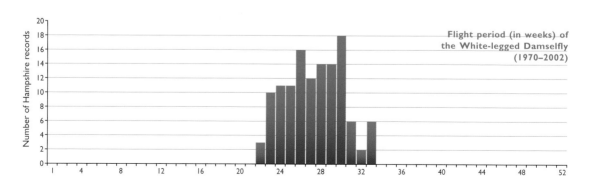

Flight period (in weeks) of the White-legged Damselfly (1970–2002)

MAJOR LOCALITIES From the previous text, it is clear that Ober Water is the only site of note in southern Hampshire, although compared with neighbouring counties, the White-legged Damselfly cannot be considered to have any major localities in Hampshire and the sub-heading 'Major Localities' is used here simply in the context of Hampshire. Similarly, the small colony around the confluence of the Blackwater and Whitewater valleys is only mentioned here because it is the only other site in the county where the species is found.

POPULATION STRENGTHS In good years, up to 100 can be found along an 800 m stretch of Ober Water, with dozens of pairs often closely packed at oviposition sites. The species tends to favour group oviposition at good sites, a practice that is thought to reduce the chances of predation. During a British Dragonfly Society meeting on the Ober Water on 21st March 1992, larvae were found along a short stretch of stream near Markway Bridge. They were found in small groups exhibiting a patchy distribution wherever mud and silt accumulates and allows growth of emergent vegetation. In North Hampshire, on the River Blackwater at Wheeler's farm, counts of up to 36 adults have been made in recent years.

FLIGHT PERIOD The species normally appears on the wing in mid to late May, is most abundant in late June and July, and the flight season is usually over by the end of August. However, with so few records in present-day Hampshire, it is difficult to determine the exact flying season, the limited data from the last few years indicating a season that is restricted to June and July.

EARLIEST/LATEST DATES Puttles Bridge on Ober Water is the location for the earliest recent record, that being 28th May 1990. The latest record comes from the Basingstoke Canal on 28th August 2000.

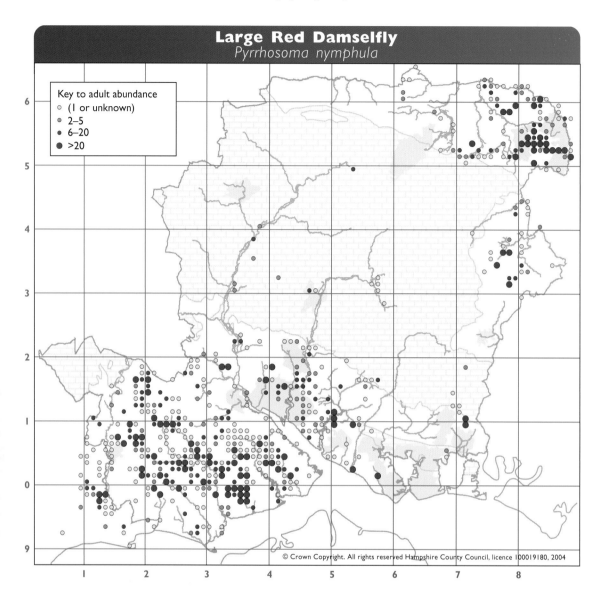

Large Red Damselfly
Pyrrhosoma nymphula

Key to adult abundance
○ (1 or unknown)
◔ 2–5
● 6–20
⬤ >20

DISTRIBUTION The distribution map shows a heavy concentration in the south-west of the county, especially in the New Forest, a considerable presence on the Tertiary rocks of the north-east, a reasonable presence on the Gault and Greensands and a very thin scatter on the chalk.

HABITAT The adult has one of the widest varieties of habitat. The habitat could best be described by where it is not found, this being on very fast-flowing streams and rivers. Typically, the Large Red Damselfly is present on ponds, ditches, slow-flowing streams and rivers as well as acid bogs, peaty pools and even brackish waters. It is often found far from water and is a 'typical' garden damselfly, even in those gardens without pools. The larvae are bottom dwellers, often defending preferred perches on dead or living vegetation. They tend to be the predominant damselfly larvae in pond mud samples.

MAJOR LOCALITIES The species is so widespread and so tolerant of water conditions that major localities would be difficult to list in Hampshire as there are so many places that would fit that category. At Eelmoor Marsh, it is the most commonly recorded damselfly over recent years and it is common throughout the Blackwater Valley. It is likely to occur throughout the county, although numbers will almost certainly be very small in ponds on the chalk.

POPULATION STRENGTHS It is not uncommon for several hundred individuals to be found at favoured sites, such as the pond at Chilworth Manor on 17th May 1990, Warren Heath Pond on 15th July 1991, at Halfpenny Green in the New Forest on 21st May 1990 and on the main lakes at Sable Waters on numerous occasions. At the last-named site, the total population at peak period must involve several hundreds. At Eelmoor Marsh SSSI, 352 were recorded on 20th June 2001 across eight of the compartments in the area, with 225 in just four compartments on 21st May 2001, but the peak count for the whole area in 1999 was 553. The maximum count from Eelmoor Marsh SSSI in one compartment was 175. However, although counts of several

hundred are not unusual, one would not expect to see 30 or 40 mating pairs at the same time on a very small pool or a mass flying over a lake, such as happens with Azure Damselflies at ponds such as Eyeworth Pond. Three-figure counts have also come from the River Blackwater, but as with other species, these populations will be shared with Surrey.

FLIGHT PERIOD This damselfly is one of the harbingers of spring, with records from April in most years. It spends the last (second) winter in diapause and there is effectively a mass emergence over two or three weeks in April and May when daylight temperatures are suitable. There is continued, sporadic emergence of fast-growing larvae through the summer and the species may be found flying in September. Records suggest that this species emerges regularly a week or so earlier in the south of the county than the north.

Adult male © Alan Hold

EARLIEST/LATEST DATES This species provides the earliest Hampshire record for any adult damselfly, this being on 5th April 1995 at Swanwick Nature Reserve. The latest record is on 24th September 1980 at Ober Water.

BEHAVIOUR After mating, females oviposit while still in tandem with males. They favour floating vegetation, such as Bog Pondweed, in which to oviposit with the females sometimes submerging and the male also submerging to the point where the water level comes to the bottom of the thorax. Such behaviour ensures that the wings remain dry above the water and the male is able to take flight should danger threaten.

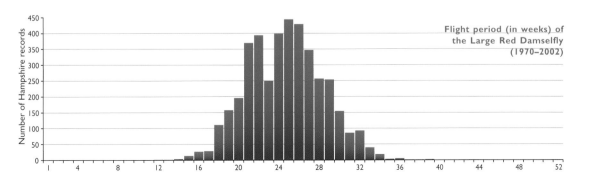

Flight period (in weeks) of the Large Red Damselfly (1970–2002)

The Dragonflies of Hampshire

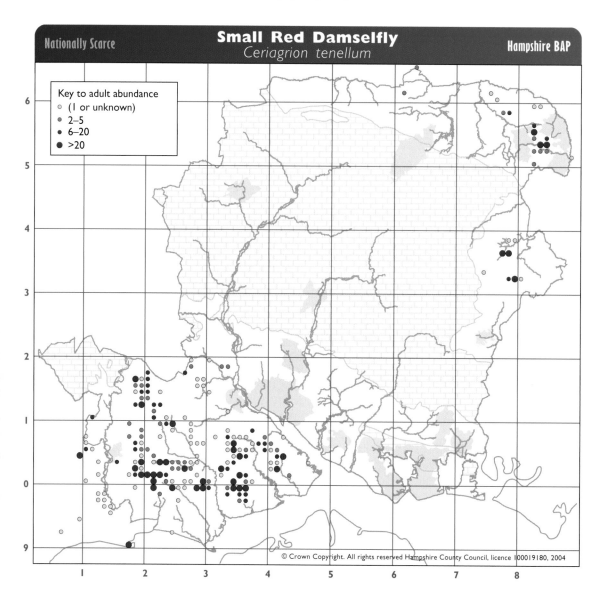

Nationally Scarce — **Small Red Damselfly** *Ceriagrion tenellum* — **Hampshire BAP**

Key to adult abundance
- ○ (1 or unknown)
- ● 2–5
- ● 6–20
- ● >20

DISTRIBUTION The principal distribution of the Small Red Damselfly in Hampshire is in the New Forest, which is a national stronghold for this nationally scarce species. In the New Forest it is widespread and often abundant at shallow pools and valley mire complexes and there are a few sites just outside the Forest perambulation where it enjoys a similar status, such as Sable Water. In some Forest streams and pools it is one of the most numerous species of Odonata.

In North Hampshire, where the heathland commons are fragmented and have not benefited from uninterrupted management for centuries, the Small Red Damselfly is a scarce insect with only five strong populations remaining. Two of these are on the Woolmer Forest heathlands, at Cranmere Bottom and Shortheath Pond, whilst the others are on heathland west of Farnborough at Eelmoor Marsh, Ancell's Pond (Fleet) and Warren Heath. Several small populations also exist on these heathlands but the available counts suggest very low numbers. The London Basin heathlands were once extensive and,

Adult male with mites © *Cindy Allen* ➤

50

two hundred years ago, would have been a landscape not unlike much of the New Forest today. We can only guess at how widespread the Small Red Damselfly and other bog specialists may have been, but the following description of Eversley Common around 1870 by the daughter of Charles Kingsley may give some idea. She wrote: "As the dry moorland sinks away into the valley we get a hollow sometimes half a mile long, filled with deep bog. Several of these bogs were some hundreds of yards in length and breadth. Just behind The Mount was a true quaking bog where, in our youth, we tried over and over again to touch the bottom with poles, but never succeeded....In the old days the bog was a rich hunting ground for the botanist and entomologist. Its surface was white with the snowy tassels of cotton-grass, orange in late autumn with the seed spikes of bog asphodel" (Kingsley, 1918). In the 1920s the bogs were drained and the heathland planted up with forestry.

A further population exists on the Gault and Greensand area. For Britain as a whole, this is of course a Nationally Scarce species, but the Hampshire populations are strong and in the New Forest it can be considered a common species.

HABITAT The Small Red Damselfly is a species of bogs and shallow heathland pools, seepages and slow-flowing ditches on wet heathland. Occasionally it is found on the margins of larger, well-vegetated ponds such as East End Gravel Pit in the New Forest. Favoured waters are commonly associated with Bog-myrtle, Marsh St John's-wort, species of grass, sedge and mats of *Sphagnum*. Such sites may also have plant communities at the water's edge that are dominated by a variety of sedges and rushes, especially Sharp-flowered Rush. At Eelmoor Marsh SSSI, the species has benefited greatly from turf scrapes, such habitats usually being colonised during the first summer.

It is a weak flier, seldom leaving the cover of vegetation, and in the New Forest, where it is often found sharing the same habitat as the Scarce Blue-tailed Damselfly and Southern Damselfly, it has been described as sedentary (Strange, 2002, unpublished). However, observations in the Farnborough area suggest that the full picture may be more complex (Hall, 1997, and unpublished observations) and there is some evidence of dispersal away from known established breeding sites. Cody Pond, an artificial pond created in 1990 around 0.5 km north of the nearest breeding site on Eelmoor Marsh, had been colonised by 1999 (Hall, 2001). A further example of dispersal has occurred to the west of Eelmoor Marsh where the remnant of the almost dried out Crookham Bog, one kilometre west of Eelmoor, had a single male in 2001, a male plus a mating pair in 2003, eight – including two pairs – three weeks later and three males in early August. Even more remarkable is the arrival of Small Red Damselflies at Ively Ponds, two artificial ponds created as part of the landscaping of Cody Technological Park in 1996. One was designed as a fish pond, the other as a wildlife pond and both quickly attracted the more mobile dragonflies, but two Small Red Damselflies were present at the wildlife pond in August 2002 and up to ten were seen on three dates in 2003. These ponds are slightly more than a kilometre north-east of the nearest breeding pool on Eelmoor Marsh, but much of the intervening land is a built environment of offices, workshops and mown lawns (C. Hall, personal observations). Recent records also exist, usually of individuals, from Fleet Pond, the Basingstoke Canal near Farnborough airfield, and other nearby sites. Larger numbers have recently been reported on Bramshill Common, where dispersal from Warren Heath or a site in Berkshire has to be considered.

The hinterland around breeding pools is also extensively used, presumably for shelter and hunting prey. However, most do not move far from water until later in the season. Observations at Ancell's Pond in July 1996 suggested that the species rarely strayed more than 30 metres from the water's edge, whereas Azure Damselflies had dispersed widely over the heathland. Vegetation that offers a varied but fairly open structure near the breeding area seems to be a requirement and may harbour more than half the population at any one time. Open areas, such as mown or heavily grazed heathland, along with very dense vegetation, are usually avoided. Oviposition is in saturated moss or on aquatic plants growing in very shallow water.

MAJOR LOCALITIES As with some other species, the Small Red Damselfly has so many sites in the New Forest that it is misleading to pick out a few localities under this heading. Examples of areas where good numbers can be found are Burley Railway Cutting, Latchmore Bottom, Crockford Stream, Peaked Hill, Millersford Bottom and Rowbarrow Pond. Cranmer Bottom, Shortheath Pond, Ancell's Farm and Eelmoor Marsh are the best sites in the north of the county.

POPULATION STRENGTHS At Burley Railway Cutting there may be hundreds and it is often the dominant species at that site with an estimated 500 adults on 22nd July 1993. The bogs and seepages along the Crockford Stream also have a population that runs into several hundreds.

More precise data is available from the north of the county, especially from Eelmoor Marsh and Ancell's Pond where monitoring has been continuous for around ten years. Ancell's Pond has produced several counts in three figures, the highest being 209 on 14th July 1996 when the pond and surrounding heathland were searched systematically. Since then the Hampshire and Isle of Wight Wildlife Trust have carried out turf scraping which has extended the amount of shallowly-flooded ground, all of which had been colonised by 2002. The largest population in the north is at Eelmoor Marsh where counts in excess of 100 are normal during peak season. The highest counts to date have been 655 on 4th August 2003, 463 on 24th July 2001 and 406 on 14th August 2002, and these counts did not cover all suitable habitat. The only other northern site with a three-figure count is Warren Heath Upper Pond where 120 were seen on 15th July 1996.

FLIGHT PERIOD The species is normally on the wing at the beginning of June in the New Forest, although it has been recorded in the third week of May. Records go on to the end of September but there was a very late record from Eelmoor Marsh on 12th October 2001, the insect appearing in good condition and not faded (Hall, 2001). Records suggest that in north Hampshire the flight season is around a week later than in the south of the county.

EARLIEST/LATEST DATES Rowbarrow Pond in the New Forest is the site for our earliest record, on 21st May 1988, whilst in the north of the county the earliest was at Ancell's Pond on 30th May 1998. The last are usually reported in late September, but an exceptionally late individual was at Eelmoor Marsh on 12th October 2001, a male that rested on Cottongrass and appeared to be in fresh condition.

BEHAVIOUR AND LIFE CYCLE The life cycle lasts two years. The species becomes active in warm weather, when males search out females at the breeding sites. Depending on temperature and weather conditions, mating may occur at any time between 10.00 hrs and 17.00 hrs and may last up to 90 minutes. Tandem pairs may be found amongst emergent vegetation at the breeding site or in nearby tall but open vegetation and the pair remain in tandem while the female oviposits into the stems or leaves of submerged or emergent plants, including Marsh St John's-wort or mosses. Larvae hatch about a month later, living among the saturated bog mosses or detritus in shallow pools or ditches for nearly two years

Adults are only active in warm sunshine. Males are territorial but tend to defend a perch rather than an area and will tolerate other males only 25 cm away. They may therefore be encountered in high densities, especially where tandem pairs and unmated females are also present. Males that move too close to another male are warned off by wing-flicking or may be chased. The damselflies are much less active in the absence of bright sun. Even on a warm July afternoon, a cloud crossing the sun will cause most to roost (Brooks, 1997 and Hall, unpublished observations).

Adults have been encountered far away from breeding sites, such as a glade within a pinewood at Eelmoor and at a garden pond in Aldershot.

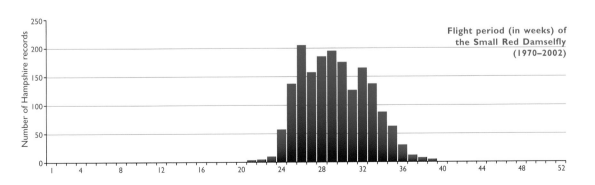

Flight period (in weeks) of the Small Red Damselfly (1970–2002)

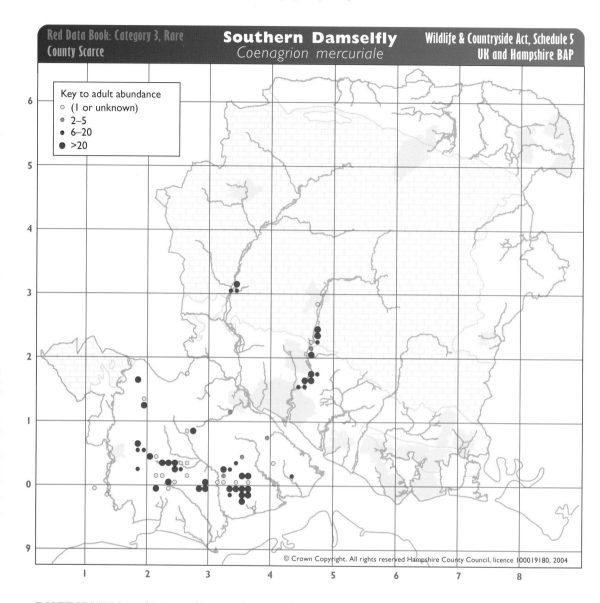

Red Data Book: Category 3, Rare
County Scarce

Southern Damselfly
Coenagrion mercuriale

Wildlife & Countryside Act, Schedule 5
UK and Hampshire BAP

Key to adult abundance
○ (I or unknown)
● 2–5
● 6–20
● >20

DISTRIBUTION This is a Red Data Book species which is endangered throughout Europe. Nationally, the Southern Damselfly is rare (Red Data Book 2, Category 3) and is protected under Schedule 5 of the Wildlife and Countryside Act of 1981 (amended in 1995) and included in the Hampshire Biodiversity Action Plan. This level of protection precludes handling and photography without a licence. Although it has suffered a 30% decline in its national distribution since 1960, a survey in 1998 showed that in the New Forest the number of sites has remained largely unchanged over this period. However, since the 1998 survey the species has disappeared from sites where it was previously known; it has not been seen recently on Ipley stream or at Blackwell Common and it is almost certainly now lost from those sites.

It has scattered populations in Dorset, Devon, South Wales, Anglesey and Hampshire with its major UK stronghold in the New Forest. Other significant populations exist on feeder streams and ditches of the lower Itchen and the upper Test, and at some of these sites, both in the New Forest and the two rivers mentioned, it can be the most abundant species of Odonata.

HABITAT *New Forest* – It is found on well-vegetated, slow-flowing mire valley streams and mire runnels, or runnels in seepages of boggy flushes on heathland. The main emergent plants are likely to be Water Mint, Floating Sweet-grass, Marsh St John's-wort, species of rush, Lesser Spearwort and Broad-leaved Pondweed, with Bog-myrtle, species of sedge and Purple Moor-grass on the surrounding banks. The need for year-round flowing water has been demonstrated recently by the virtual loss of one site where the ground dried out during a summer drought. Although Southern Damselflies can be found breeding in New Forest streams with *p*H as low as 5, the strongest colonies occur where the water is enriched to *p*H 6.4 to 7 by springs fed from underlying calcareous formations or flows through outcrops of the shelly Headon Beds. Many of the sites are kept free of encroaching scrub by the feeding and trampling of Commoners' animals.

River sites – The two major chalk streams in Hampshire, the Test and the Itchen, both support colonies along the ditches and minor carriers associated with the old water-meadow irrigation systems in the flood plains. Restricted access to these two rivers, internationally renowned for their excellent fishing, makes it difficult to monitor all potentially suitable sites. However, extensive surveys have been conducted on parts of the Itchen over recent years and a number of colonies have been located along the stretch from Twyford Moors to just south of the M27 at Mansbridge. A partial survey of potential sites along the Test in 1988 located only one colony in water-meadows at an exclusively private site south of Stockbridge, and then two further small colonies were found down-river in 2002. It is possible that there may be other small colonies yet to be found on the Test. The sites on both rivers are all associated with secondary carriers and the ditches and channels of old water-meadow irrigation systems that still carry water throughout the year. The flow of these water courses is slow to moderate, thus allowing a build-up of loose silt amongst the emergent vegetation along their margins. The emergent vegetation found at these sites includes Reed Sweet-grass, Branched Bur-reed, Water-cress, Reed Canary-grass and Yellow Iris. It was also noted that these sites were invariably poached by cattle that came to these water courses to eat the luxuriant vegetation, especially Reed Sweet-grass.

Samantha Jacobs, working in Itchen Valley Country Park, studied the nocturnal habits of the species for a BSc Dissertation at Sparsholt College. She found that although it could not be statistically proven, Southern Damselflies move further away from water at night, the mean distance from water at night roosts being almost double the distance of insects found by day. Samantha's work also found that different habitats were used for night roosts, Hard Rush being the most favoured plant used, followed by Tufted Hair-grass. Common Bent, Hairy Sedge, Lesser Pond-sedge, Perennial Rye-grass, Rough Meadow-grass and Yorkshire Fog were also used for roosting, one interesting discovery being that distance from the ground was of less importance than distance up the stem of the plant. Regardless of the species of vegetation used, there was a tendency to roost at around a similar percentage of the various plants' heights rather than the same height from the ground beneath. The mean figure for this roosting position was 88.4% of the stem's height.

The same Dissertation found that where Southern Damselflies were found in the Country Park, Bog Pondweed, Fool's Water-cress, Marsh St John's-wort, Water-cress and Water Mint were the commonest plants in the water, whilst Black-Bog-rush, Jointed Rush, Reed Canary-grass and Reed Sweet-grass formed the bulk of the bankside vegetation.

MAJOR LOCALITIES *New Forest* – The Crockford Stream/Peaked Hill complex is the most important site in the New Forest, with strong colonies at Round Hill, Mill Lawn/Burley Rocks, Gypsey Hollies and Lay Gutter Valley. Good numbers have also been seen at a spot near Burley.

River sites – On the River Itchen, Itchen Valley Country Park holds the largest population, but there is also an important population on the River Test.

POPULATION STRENGTHS The strongest and densest colonies occur in the south in the Crockford/Peaked Hill areas where the total number of insects counted on Crockford Stream, its tributaries and associated runnels is regularly around 2,000 at the optimum emergence period. However, mark/recapture studies indicate that the number emerging over the whole season is likely to be three or four times greater than this. Other colonies classified as 'strong' (>100 insects recorded) are located at Round Hill, Burley Lawn, Gypsey Hollies and Lay Gutter Valley. At the other end of the scale, there are several sites that have persisted for decades with observed numbers down to single figures. Although the Forest is well covered by recorders, the large

Two pairs ovipositing © Alan Hold ➤ *overleaf*

area and complex terrain mean that there is still scope for discovery of new sites. Thus the 33 recorded sites include four new ones from a 1998 survey, with another added in 1999 and a strong colony found on the western edge of the Forest in 2002.

The largest colony found to date on the chalk rivers is within the Itchen Valley Country Park where recent population studies suggest that this colony easily matches the population at Crockford, in that upwards of 5,000 individuals are likely to emerge over a whole season. A number of other Itchen valley sites hold medium-sized colonies (30–99 individuals). However, further monitoring may reveal larger numbers. The only known site in 1998 on the Test may be regarded as being a strong colony as an estimated 300+ individuals were present.

FLIGHT PERIOD In general the flight period extends from mid-May to the beginning of August with a peak emergence around the end of June and the beginning of July, varying somewhat with the weather pattern. However, there is evidence that the flight period is slowly extending at both ends, possibly an indication of global warming. Thus at Upper Peaked Hill, the earliest emergence, usually of males, can now be at the end of the first week of May, given good weather, compared with the last week of May some 20 years ago. Single males have been recorded regularly into September, and in 2002 the last breeding pairs were recorded on 7th September and the last insect (a male) on 29th September. In 2003, the main flight season in the Forest was over well before the end of August, but single males at both Lower Crockford and Peaked Hill were present on the 4th, 17th and 25th September, having survived a week of strong winds, heavy showers and a frost. It is of interest that both the earliest and latest insects recorded on the Peaked Hill stream over the last 20 years have been recorded within the same stretch of approximately 100–150 metres of water.

The limited data from the Itchen and Test sites would suggest that the flight period of these colonies does not have a great variance from those in the New Forest, although further research may reveal interesting comparisons.

The earliest recorded insects are usually males, and males survive a week or two later at the end of the season.

EARLIEST/LATEST DATES Both the earliest and latest dates come from Peaked Hill in the New Forest, the earliest being on 6th May in both 1999 and 2003 (a freshly emerged individual was seen on this last date with another male that was fully coloured and so must have been out for at least one day). The latest date is the 29th September 2002.

BEHAVIOUR AND LIFE CYCLE The Southern Damselfly in Britain has a semi-voltine development, i.e. it has a two year life cycle and may be regarded as a summer species in that larvae over-winter in more than one instar and do not have a synchronised emergence. When ready to emerge, the final instar larvae seek open slow-flowing sections of the stream that have tall emergent vegetation with rigid upright stems such as rushes. Emergence takes place on these rigid stems in the morning, usually about 5 cm above the surface of the water, and is probably influenced by sunlight and temperature. After a few hours the bodies and wings of the newly-emerged adults have hardened and they take their maiden flight into nearby vegetation. Adults spend about a week close to the stream where they feed and roost until reaching maturity.

Once mature, and on sunny days that are not too windy, adults may be found along favourable streams from mid-morning until mid-afternoon, with peak activity normally around mid-day. After forming a tandem pair, copulation takes place in the surrounding vegetation for about 20 minutes. The tandem pair return to the stream where submerged or semi-submerged soft-tissue plants, such as Marsh St John's-wort and Bog Pondweed in the New Forest sites and Lesser Water-parsnip and Water-cress on the chalk stream sites, are to be found in the un-shaded, open areas of shallow, slow-flowing water. It has been noticed that the females test the plants for suitability before partially submerging themselves to place, on average, about 150 ova in the soft outer tissue of the selected plants about 4 cm below the water surface. When population densities are high, females will completely submerge whilst in tandem to enable them to oviposit well below the water's surface.

There is no diapause in the ova stage of the Southern Damselfly and ova hatch about four to five weeks later. Around 90% of this damselfly's life cycle is spent in the larval stage amongst the submerged vegetation. They prey upon small aquatic invertebrate larvae that include those of midges and mayfly. Low winter temperatures have an effect on the availability of prey and this probably restricts the growth of larvae during the winter months. The larvae pass through 13 instars before emergence.

Mark-release-capture schemes indicate that adults typically live between one to two weeks, although several individuals have been noted to have a life span in excess of 50 days. Adults are regarded as being relatively sedentary in that many do not move more than 25 metres in their lifetime. However, some individuals have been recorded travelling over 1.5 km across what is regarded as unsuitable habitat. The implication for conservation is that natural migration to suitable sites would be extremely limited.

The 30% decline in this species nationally is happily not mirrored in Hampshire. Recent studies suggest that the species is "doing well" in the county and may well not have experienced the declines noted elsewhere.

ADDITIONAL NOTES The Southern Damselfly has been given individual species protection in both Britain and Europe. It is listed in the Berne and Bonn Conventions and the European Habitats Directive, besides being deemed '*Rare*' in the British Red Data Book and given protection under Schedule 5 of the Wildlife and Countryside Act 1981 (as amended in 1995). It is included in the British Biodiversity Action Plan (BAP), so a Species Action Plan (SAP) was created to be co-ordinated by a Steering Group set up in 1996 consisting of the Wildlife Trusts (lead partner), the Environment Agency, the British Dragonfly Society, English Nature, the Countryside Council for Wales and researchers from Liverpool University.

As the Southern Damselfly is a rare creature, it has been the subject of published works by a number of local researchers including: (Hold, 1997), (Strange, 1999), (Winsland (1985) and a series of studies (Jenkins, 1991, 1995, 1998, 2001).

For the SAP to be completed a great deal of further research was needed to establish the ecological requirements of the Southern Damselfly. The Steering Group commissioned a PhD study by Bethan Purse of Liverpool University for an in-depth investigation of the species at Crockford Stream in the New Forest. The study resulted in an R & D Technical report published by the Environment Agency (Purse, 2002). Bethan's study, besides confirming and enhancing much of the knowledge gained piece-meal by previous workers, provides a comprehensive understanding of the Southern Damselfly at its major New Forest stronghold. A similar PhD study has been commissioned to investigate the species at the major chalk stream site in the Itchen Valley Country Park.

Habitat requirements – In Britain, the Southern Damselfly requires the following habitat features. Small watercourses with small to moderate permanent flow, such as narrow streams on heathlands and small ditches adjacent to chalk rivers, that are fed by springs supplying a permanent flow of water with a high minimum temperature in the winter. Water in these streams will warm up rapidly during periods of sunshine. These waters should be unpolluted, with a high oxygen content and low nutrient values to restrict algae growth.

Watercourses should be open without shading from overhanging vegetation. The vegetation cover of the stream should be less than 0.5 metres in height and include soft-stemmed submerged plants for oviposition along with emergent plants that have rigid stems for emergence sites. Streams and ditches supporting breeding Southern Damselflies have been noted as having shallow deposits of silt or peat.

Site management – The Environment Agency has issued guidance for the management and creation of Southern Damselfly sites that include the following recommendations.

- Set up grazing regimes, with cattle during the summer and horses all year round, in order to produce poaching of the watercourse margins.
- Remove bankside vegetation, such as Bog-myrtle, herbs, rushes, scrub and trees by hand on a rotational basis but maintaining some shelter close by.
- Channels should be cleared by hand in short sections on a rotational basis, maintaining a broad fringe of vegetation on the chalk stream ditches.
- Maintain spring and summer water levels in the water-meadow ditches with the use of drop-board weirs.
- Manage land adjacent to watercourses so that nutrient run-off is minimised to prevent pollution of channels.

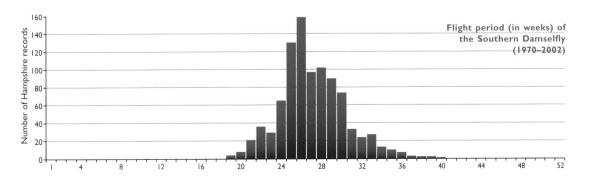

Flight period (in weeks) of
the **Southern Damselfly**
(1970–2002)

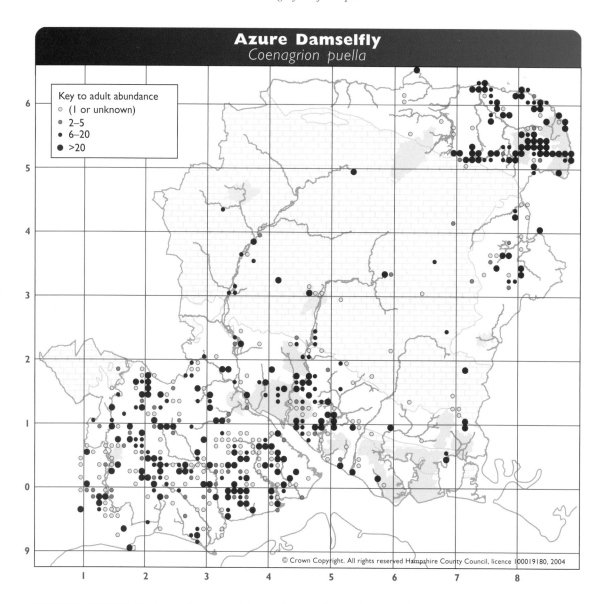

Azure Damselfly
Coenagrion puella

Key to adult abundance
- ○ (1 or unknown)
- ● 2–5
- ● 6–20
- ● >20

DISTRIBUTION This is one of the most widely spread species of dragonfly in Hampshire. The map shows just how widespread the species is on the Tertiary rocks, with a heavy concentration in the New Forest. There is a thin scatter over most of the central chalk where it is found along river margins, in garden ponds which may hold a not inconsiderable population, and on artificial lakes such as Alresford Pond and Avington Lake, often quite well into the high chalk. The species rapidly colonised a small dew pond on top of Stockbridge Down, and a small suburban pool in Winchester, on the high chalk, holds a large number in view of the size of the pool in question. Generally, numbers on the chalk do not begin to compare with those found on the rocks that lie to the north and south, but if more observers looked at small garden ponds on the chalk, it is possible that this species may show a scattering of records across the whole area. Over geological types other than chalk in Hampshire, it may well be the most numerous of the dragonfly family.

HABITAT The Azure Damselfly is found in a very wide range of habitats, including lakes, ponds, streams, rivers, peaty pools, ditches and, as stated in the previous section, garden ponds. It generally favours those areas with dense vegetation and is often encountered resting or feeding in water meadows, hedgerows and other habitat that is some way from water.

MAJOR LOCALITIES This is one of those species where there are so many localities that would fit the adjective 'major' that it is misleading to attempt a full list. The following section on 'Population Strengths' will give a few examples of important sites, but they should not be taken as the only ones.

POPULATION STRENGTHS In the early summer at many Hampshire sites, this species will be the commonest of the 'blue' damselflies. On a sunny day, most good sites will have between 20 and 100 individuals in and around the margins and at the best sites, numbers will soar well beyond these figures and involve several hundreds of adults, and at a complex such as Sable Waters the peak population almost certainly runs into four figures. On 24th June 2003, the count around just the water margins at Sable Waters was in excess of 500 and the day's population for the water complex there must have been at least twice as large as that figure. Regular counts of well over 100 are possible at sites such as Shortheath Pond, Eyeworth Pond, Eelmoor Flash on the Basingstoke Canal, Eelmoor Marsh, Ash Embankment by the Basingstoke Canal and the River Blackwater, Tucker's Bridge Pond, Furzey Pool, Swanwick Nature Reserve and the Itchen Valley Country Park, and these are only a selection of sites as examples from different parts of Hampshire. An old garden swimming pool in Winchester, measuring some 10 m by 6 m and converted by the owners into a wildlife pond, held up to 50 ovipositing pairs that could be seen at the same time.

Pair in cop © *John Taverner*

Counts have also exceeded 500 at Hook Common Pond (1,000+ in 1993, 1995 and 1997), on the Basingstoke Canal at Claycart Flash in July 1989 and Ash Lock in May 1994, and at Linbrook Lake in May 1992. At Eelmoor Marsh SSSI, the peak count was 466 in 2000. A count of 1,000 was also estimated at Bourley Ponds in 1996. There seems to be a certain unwillingness amongst both lepidopterists and odonatists to estimate numbers when they pass a certain point, and it is much more difficult to count insects in comparison with birds, but if more effort were to be put into this aspect of study, counts of Azure Damselflies going well into three figures would probably come from many Hampshire waters, with a day's count possibly going into four figures at the best sites. David and Jean Dell carry out such counts, and the following is a selection of their work: 1,400 at Hook Common Pond on 23rd June 1995 and 1,250 there on 23rd June 1997; 1,000 at Bourley Ponds on 27th June 1996; 950 on the Basingstoke Canal at Watts Common on 31st May 1997; 825 at Ash Embankment on 28th May 1994; 700 at Ancell's Farm on 16th June 1996.

FLIGHT PERIOD The flight period for this species usually starts at the beginning of May and extends until the end of August. The peak tends to be in May and June with numbers steadily falling away during the latter part of summer. Data for this species suggest that the flying season is commencing a week earlier in the north of the county in recent years.

EARLIEST/LATEST DATES Our earliest record is 29th April 1993 on the Basingstoke Canal at Ash Embankment, and our latest on 19th September 1991 at Eversley Gravel Pits.

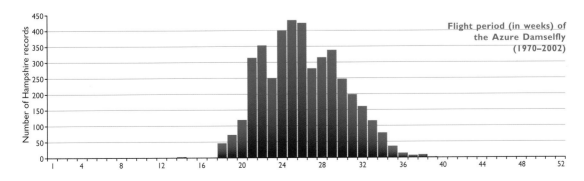

Flight period (in weeks) of the Azure Damselfly (1970–2002)

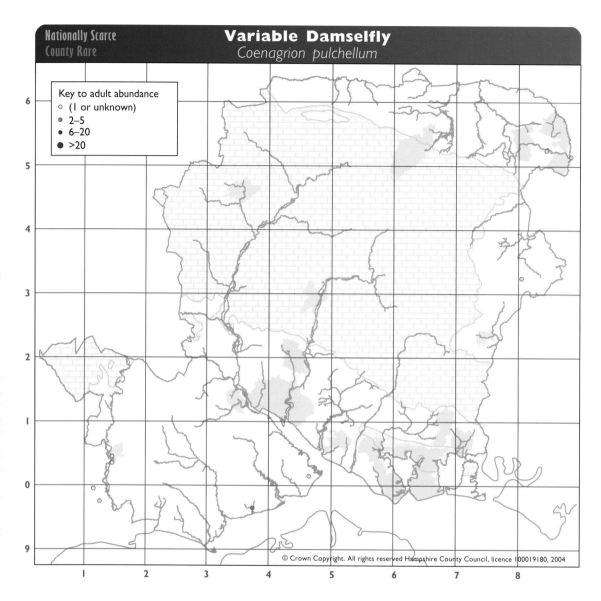

Nationally Scarce
County Rare

Variable Damselfly
Coenagrion pulchellum

Key to adult abundance
○ (1 or unknown)
• 2–5
● 6–20
⬤ >20

DISTRIBUTION The only site in Hampshire where this species is at present suspected to breed is at a private lake on the edge of the New Forest. Anecdotal reports from Itchen Valley Country Park have not been substantiated in spite of extensive surveys of the well-vegetated ditches and streams by several observers over the past decade. There have been recent records from the Surrey part of the Basingstoke Canal and David and Jean Dell found one on the Hampshire part of the canal on 26th May 1999 and 22nd May 2000. There are past records of this species being present in some numbers on the Hampshire and Surrey parts of the canal and these will be covered under a subsequent sub-heading.

HABITAT This species prefers sites with emergent vegetation, including fens, mesotrophic ponds and lakes, ditches, canals and peaty pools in bogs.

MAJOR LOCALITIES The Hampshire site where breeding is suspected has a large private lake with a well vegetated, sheltered but ungrazed perimeter that provides a habitat that does not exist on the neighbouring open New Forest. David

Winsland reports that prior to the storm of 1989, the Variable Damselfly was abundant along the southern edge of this site. He believes that the loss of trees, by storm and timber extraction, destroyed both shelter and emergent bankside vegetation. The species can no longer be found at this site, although it may persist on other sections of the lake to which public access is difficult (Winsland, 1994a).

POPULATION STRENGTHS Mainly due to restricted access to the only known site, records for this species are few. As only a small section of the lake's perimeter can be seen from the public road, it is possible that much of the colony has never been located. The few records, mainly anecdotal (only one record card in 1992 being submitted during the six year period of the Key Sites Project), suggest a very small population, but this cannot be regarded as reliable. Further monitoring is required to obtain a true picture of this damselfly's status both at this site and in the county as a whole.

FLIGHT PERIOD Since there is so little reliable data from the county, it is not possible to make any statements on this subject with any accuracy.

EARLIEST/LATEST DATES The earliest date we have is 21st May 1992 at Sowley Pond and the latest on 8th June 1982 at Sowley and 12th June 1984 at Ringwood.

ADDITIONAL NOTES The past status of this species on the Basingstoke Canal is confused and may well remain unclear, but it is possible that it was present in some strength. The earliest records come from A.W. Richards, although he does not always distinguish between the Hampshire and Surrey portions of the canal. In May 1939 he recorded the species on 27th May and stated that it "occurs along the Basingstoke Canal, but not commonly" (Richards, 1939). In 1940 he recorded the Variable Damselfly as common all along the Basingstoke Canal. Twenty years later he appears to have changed his mind because on record cards prepared for the Camberley Natural History Society he lists only two sites for the species, these being Alice Holt and the Basingstoke Canal where it was "reported by Col. Fraser". In the remarks column in those record cards Richards writes: "I have never found this species in the areas mentioned. It is easy to confuse it with blue

Adult male © Alan Hold

female *C. puella*". So, the evidence of Richards is not wholly clear. The next canal records come from Southampton N.H.S. field trips, where the species was reported on 14th June 1969 along the Odiham to Greywell stretch. On 26th May 1972, another Southampton N.H.S. field trip reported "swarms of damselflies" on the canal near Odiham, especially Variable and Large Red Damselflies. There is one other source that suggests the species was present on the canal in the 1960s, although this refers to the Surrey part, this being old Nature Conservancy files which refer to records of the Variable Damselfly "before 1971" (Savant, 1977).

John Pontin, a very experienced entomologist who is familiar with the species, recorded two Variable Damselflies on the Surrey portion of the canal on 11th June 1992 and a female on 22nd June 1995, both on the Ash Embankment that is very close to the Hampshire border. Extensive searches by David and Jean Dell along the Hampshire section produced only the records given above in the 'Distribution' sub-section, so it would appear that even if the species had been present in some strength in the past, there is at best a relic population left on the Hampshire section of the canal.

The species has also been reported from Fleet Pond where the NCC Invertebrates Site Register from the early 1980s states for Fleet Pond that "The notable species lost are *Ischnura pumilio* and *Coenagrion pulchellum*".

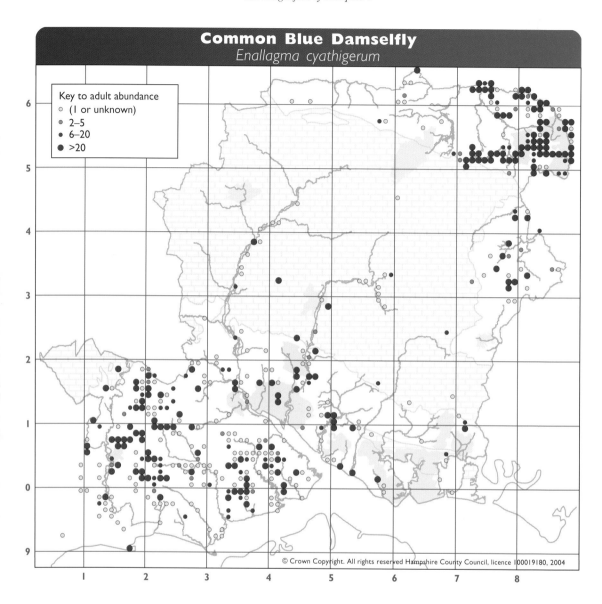

Common Blue Damselfly
Enallagma cyathigerum

Key to adult abundance
- ○ (1 or unknown)
- • 2–5
- • 6–20
- ● >20

DISTRIBUTION This species is widespread in Hampshire, although it is possibly not quite so widespread as the Azure Damselfly since the latter appears on any number of small ponds that the Common Blue Damselfly avoids. On the central chalk, for instance, where both species are far less numerous than they are on the rocks to the north and south, the Azure Damselfly seems to readily colonise garden pools and small artificial waters whereas the Common Blue Damselfly is frequently absent from such places. It has the classic Hampshire distribution for dragonflies, being widespread both south and north of the chalk, especially in the New Forest and around the Basingstoke Canal area, with a scattering of records in the Wealden anticline and along the main chalk rivers and just odd records from the high chalk.

HABITAT The Common Blue Damselfly breeds in open ponds and lakes, and canals and rivers of slow to moderate flow. It can be very abundant in the most oligotrophic and acidic conditions as well as being common and widespread in lowland and even eutrophic conditions elsewhere. It is an early coloniser and is often amongst the first species to visit a newly dug garden pond, although on the central chalk this feature is not so evident as the opening paragraph shows. Amongst the species' favourite spots, often well out from the water's edge, are the dead stems of aquatic plants and the floating leaves of Pondweeds and various plants commonly referred to as Water-lilies. The best habitat for this species is open water with submerged plants such as Rigid Hornwort and Water-milfoils.

MAJOR LOCALITIES There are far too many sites that would fit this category to name them. Sufficient to say that the Common Blue Damselfly lives up to its name on most water bodies in Hampshire and under ideal conditions may be seen in large numbers at many sites. Some of the sites where particularly large counts have been made are named below.

POPULATION STRENGTHS At many of the favoured sites, this species may be seen swarming over the open water. Regular counts of over 100 have been made at places such as Eyeworth Pond, Bourley Ponds at Aldershot, Shortheath Pond, Bramshill Plantation, Ash Embankment, Waterslade Bottom, Slufters Pond and Linbrook Lake. It has been reported on a number

of occasions that the estimated population at various sites was over 500 individuals, such sites including Cranmer Pond at Longmoor in July 1996, Eelmoor Flash on the Basingstoke Canal in July 1991, Poulner Lake in May 1989 and Linbrook Lake in May 1992, whilst in the chapter dealing with the human influence on dragonfly habitat, it has already been noted that the total population on Ivy Lake and Elingham Lake at Blashford must have run into several thousands on 20th June 2003 (see page 8). In the north-east, the old gravel pits in the Blackwater valley also hold considerable populations.

FLIGHT PERIOD This damselfly has a long flying season, beginning in mid-May and lasting until late September and occasionally continuing into October. There is a tendency for the species to be on the wing a week earlier in the south of the county compared with the north.

Female eating midge © *Cindy Allen*

EARLIEST/LATEST DATES Our earliest record is 5th May 1990 at Poulner Lake, whilst the latest is 2nd October 1996 at Bourley Ponds.

BEHAVIOUR Large 'swarms' of males can often be seen hovering over open water and for the casual observer such behaviour is difficult to understand. However, this takes place at prime breeding sites where vegetation lies just below the water's surface. It is a sure sign that females are ovipositing underwater into the vegetation below. The females oviposit by carrying a pocket of air between their wings and the hairs on their body. They can remain submerged for around thirty minutes before floating to the surface where they are retrieved by the hovering males.

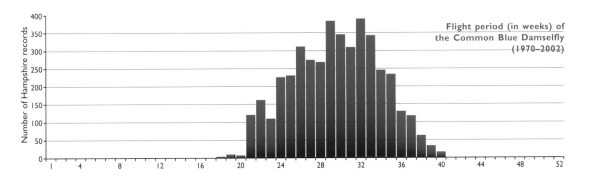

Flight period (in weeks) of the **Common Blue Damselfly** (1970–2002)

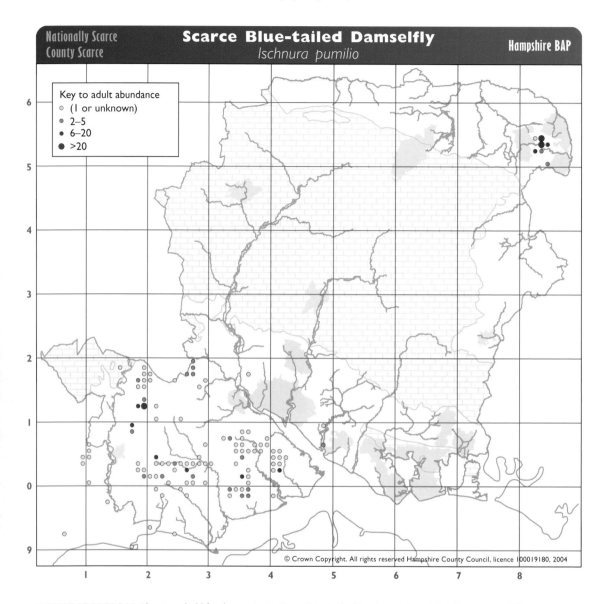

Nationally Scarce
County Scarce

Scarce Blue-tailed Damselfly
Ischnura pumilio

Hampshire BAP

Key to adult abundance
○ (1 or unknown)
◦ 2–5
● 6–20
● >20

DISTRIBUTION The stronghold for the species in Hampshire is the New Forest where it has been recorded for many years. In recent times, reasonable numbers have been seen at a number of sites including Black Gutter, Burley disused railway line, Crockford and Peaked Hill complex, Mill Lawn, Millersford Bottom, Latchmore Bottom, Rooks Bridge, South Weirs and White Moor Bottom. However, since the early 1990s, both the sites and numbers of adults have decreased quite noticeably so that it is now 'lost' from most of the sites shown on the above map. It is still seen regularly at Latchmore Bottom.

One recent discovery that is rather interesting is the occurrence of an immature female *aurantiaca* at Old Bursledon Nature Haven that was found and photographed by John Horne. Nearby, on 20th June 2001, at a tiny seepage on Hamble Common, over ten Scarce Blue-tailed Damselflies were discovered and the species has been seen in subsequent years. The site is just across Southampton Water opposite the nearest known New Forest sites so it is just possible that the individuals in question could have originated from there.

The distribution is limited by the availability of suitable habitat in the county. Away from the New Forest there is a lack of the shallow seepage habitat. In North-east Hampshire, the only old records traced are from Fleet Pond just after the Second World War

Adult male in New Forest mire © *Alan Hold*

when the species was observed over a period from 1947 to 1949, though the Thames Basin heathlands before enclosure of the commons would have had habitats similar to those of the New Forest today, and it is conceivable that this damselfly was fairly widespread before 1850. At Fleet Pond, the species was first reported on 28th May 1947 by A.W. Richards, who had a specimen confirmed by Cynthia Longfield. The year 1949 was particularly good when it was present "in profusion", the species emerging on 14th May with ovipositing pairs still present in September. During the winter of 1949–1950 the military authorities sprayed insecticides on the marshes to control mosquitoes and the Scarce Blue-tailed Damselfly was not seen again (based on record cards by A.W. Richards, held by Camberley Natural History Society). The most likely location would have been the marshes and wet heathland around the southern end of the lake.

However, in July 1999 the species was discovered at Eelmoor Marsh SSSI by Adrian Hine (Hine, 2000), 21 being counted on 19th July and 13 the next day, though a count of 20 Blue-tailed Damselflies in 1997 at exactly the same spot may have included some of the rarer species. Searches in 2000 confirmed that the species was still present and then successful breeding was proved in 2001. These Eelmoor damselflies were mostly in the species' preferred habitat of turf scrapes with three amongst rushy seepages.

The Eelmoor colony is now known to extend into two one-kilometre squares (SU8353 and SU8453), though total numbers in peak season may only be around 50.

The earliest records for Hampshire are contained in a series of letters between J.C. and C.W. Dale and R. MacLachlan that give details of specimens taken near Lyndhurst in August 1820 (Fraser, 1941). In the *Dragonflies of the British Isles* by Cynthia Longfield, published in 1937, she describes it as a very rare damselfly found in one, possibly two counties in England. The county where she could be sure it still occurred was Hampshire.

Just outside the north-west of the county there are recent records from Berkshire and Surrey and there is an isolated record of one at Farlington on 29th July 2001, an *aurantiaca* female examined in the hand by A. Twyford (Parr, 2001). This report in *Atropos* suggested that for a species with strong dispersal powers, the Farlington insect could have come from New Forest colonies, but it was also suggested that as migrants such as Red-veined Darter and Lesser Emperor were seen in southern Britain in that year, the Farlington specimen could have been an immigrant.

HABITAT In the New Forest the shallow, slow-moving flushes draining the main bogs appear to be the most natural habitat for the species and these may act as reservoirs for dispersal to other areas. Flushes and seepages flowing into streams on the New Forest grazed lawns and heaths kept open by grazing and ditching are the most favoured habitat. Sporadic ditching activities have in the past resulted in the creation of suitable microhabitat conditions, which have been reflected by increased abundance of the species. However, such conditions deteriorate in time and lack of ditch management in the Forest may have contributed to its current relative scarcity in some parts (D. Winsland, pers.comm.). Similar microhabitat is also found around the shallow periphery of ponds kept open by repeated grazing and trampling from livestock.

Three habitats have been utilised at Eelmoor Marsh SSSI, all sharing similarities with the New Forest sites. The colony discovered by Hine was utilising an area of rushy swamp and very shallowly-flooded ground. The species was subsequently found along boggy ditches with very shallow, slow-moving or almost still water, and on shallowly-flooded turf cuts with seepages in wet heathland. Monitoring in 2000–2001 suggests the last-named is the preferred habitat and that new turf cuts attract the species in the summer following their creation if shallow pools or seepages form (Hall, 2001). Eelmoor Marsh is an actively managed Nature Reserve which receives light, year-round grazing by cattle and horses.

The southern distribution in Britain, which also represents the northern limit of its range, suggests that its distribution may be limited by temperature. It is predominantly a Mediterranean species, which has been reported to colonise northwards and eastwards in favourable seasons. The Scarce Blue-tailed Damselfly can survive in transient habitat conditions and is able to exploit newly created freshwater habitat in a manner not apparently utilised by any other Odonata species in Britain. Wherever it occurs, it favours shallow water with slow movement, conditions which are often susceptible to drying out. The shallow water conditions that make up its habitat warm up rapidly during summer and the spring-fed seepages remain ice-free in all but the coldest winters. Depressions which retain water throughout the summer, such as tractor ruts and calverts amongst gravel workings, offer similar conditions and are also colonised.

Most of the sites where it occurs exhibit some degree of disturbance, which seems positively beneficial to the maintenance of the right habitat conditions. This can take various forms. Grazing and trampling by livestock in shallow water is characteristic of many sites in the New Forest preventing the encroachment of vegetation which would displace Scarce Blue-tailed Damselflies. This aspect of the habitat has to be carefully considered in the formulation of conservation management plans.

MAJOR LOCALITIES One of the largest populations in the New Forest is along the Latchmore Brook, which has an adjacent bog complex.

POPULATION STRENGTHS Lucas, who observed the species in the New Forest from 1901, recorded observations over a number of years and found that colonies appeared to go through considerable fluctuations. In 1926, following several years of fruitless searching, he concluded that it was extinct in the area. However, in subsequent years F.C. Fraser and Dr. F. Haines rediscovered sizeable colonies (Fraser, 1941). These fluctuations still appear to occur to the present day.

Habitat disturbance is beneficial to this species and needs to be considered in site management. Grazing of vegetation and trampling in shallow water should be encouraged wherever possible. At quarry sites the activities of motor bike scrambling and four-wheel drive vehicles, whilst appearing undesirable, have prevented the encroachment of vegetation and have created water-filled wheel tracks for colonisation. It is relatively easy for conservation activities to reproduce this by removing choking vegetation from flush lines, and to create new pools and ponds on bare substrates suitable for colonisation. However, because the suitability of new habitat declines, it is important to clear and manage such temporary wetlands on a rotational basis. In particular, it is important to ensure the perpetuation of bare, fine substrates and the restriction of submergent and emergent macrophytes (especially aggressive species such as Great Reedmace). The maintenance of soft-stemmed grasses and rushes at an early stage of succession is also advantageous. The conservation of such habitat is also important for a range of other flora and fauna which depend on similar specialised conditions.

The number of sites with this specialised habitat is very low and this inevitably limits the availability for colonisation. It is for this reason that where such sites occur they should be given a high level of conservation priority.

At Eelmoor Marsh, Chris Hall counted 21 on 15th June 2000, including four females, one of which was the immature *aurantiaca* form. Though very localised in this specialised habitat, the Eelmoor population in 2003 has extended its range and has attempted to colonise two sites outside of the SSSI. Counts at Eelmoor have steadily increased to a maximum of 70 on 16th June 2003, which is very high for Hampshire.

FLIGHT PERIOD At Eelmoor Marsh the recorded flight period is early June to mid-August. For Hampshire as a whole, the period from June to August inclusive forms the flying season.

EARLIEST/LATEST DATES White Moor Bottom, in the New Forest, provides the earliest date, this being 28th May 1989, whilst the latest date is 3rd September 1981 at Stonyford Pond.

BEHAVIOUR AND LIFE CYCLE The Scarce Blue-tailed Damselfly has a one-year life cycle which makes it able to adapt well to the changing habitat conditions it encounters. To survive in shallow water habitat where conditions are subject to periodic drought a damselfly must be able to colonise, mate and disperse before conditions become unsuitable. The species appears able to survive in such habitat, which many other dragonfly species find unattractive. Rapid larval development and a generation time of one year followed by dispersal appear to be the key to its survival. Adults spend a lot of time resting or flying in amongst vegetation, yet on very warm, sunny days with little or no cloud cover, some individuals have been observed to change behaviour. Adults of both sexes and different age classes have been observed to revert to a very direct and positive flight vertically upwards until they are lost from sight (Fox, 1989; Cham, 1993). This dispersal flight, which maybe assisted by rising thermals, enables individuals to reach higher levels where prevailing winds can carry them away, hopefully to form new colonies.

On rare occasions, mistaken tandem pairings with females of the Small Red Damselfly have been observed in the New Forest where the species coincide.

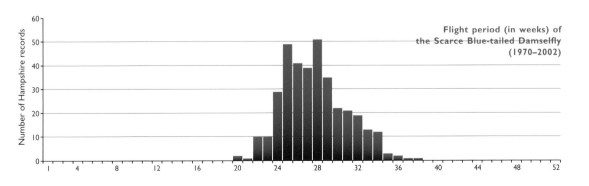

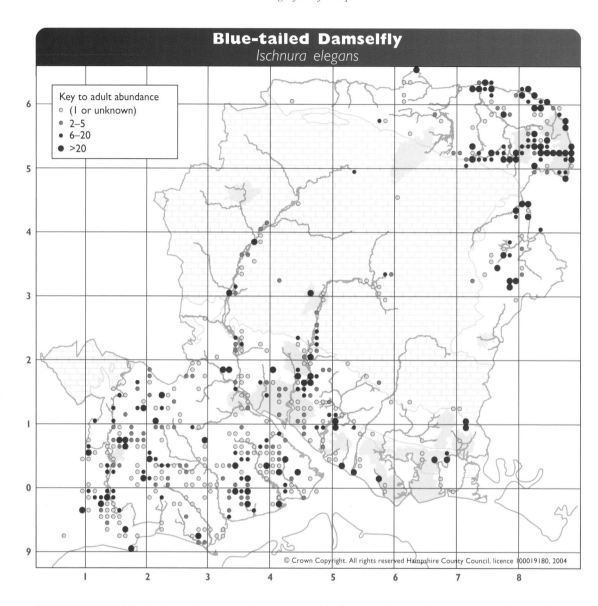

Blue-tailed Damselfly
Ischnura elegans

Key to adult abundance
- ◦ (1 or unknown)
- • 2–5
- • 6–20
- ● >20

DISTRIBUTION This is another species that is widespread in the county having the 'Classic Hampshire Distribution' with the largest populations on the Tertiary rocks. In these areas it is common and, if a waterbody has dragonflies, then it is highly probable that the Blue-tailed Damselfly will be amongst their number. Even on the chalk, this species has been found at some small pools and a survey of garden ponds would probably reveal even more sites.

HABITAT The Blue-tailed Damselfly breeds in a wide range of habitats, including ponds, lakes, moderate to slow-flowing rivers, canals, ditches, peaty pools and garden ponds. It is most numerous in neutral to eutrophic waters. It prefers well-vegetated wetlands but it is tolerant of less luxuriant growth and is an early coloniser of new habitat that is made available. It will survive in brackish conditions and is tolerant of slightly polluted water. However, the acid waters of the New Forest and other heathlands are not its favourite habitat; although widespread in the Forest, it is not seen there in numbers that compare with many parts of the county.

MAJOR LOCALITIES As with a few other species, there are so many localities that would qualify for the term 'major' that there is no point in producing a list. This damselfly is to be found on most water bodies throughout the county, especially those with good stands of marginal vegetation. This species will be found near water on dull and overcast days when no other damselflies are on the wing.

POPULATION STRENGTHS It is not unusual to find this species in numbers exceeding 100 at many of the larger water bodies, including Holbury Mill Pond, the Itchen Valley Country Park, Eversley Gravel Pit, Holt Pond on the River Wey, Needs Ore pools and various locations along the Basingstoke Canal and the River Blackwater. On several occasions the population of this damselfly has been estimated to be over 500; such high counts occurred at Ash Embankment on the Basingstoke Canal in July 1992 and 1994, at Linbrook Lake in May 1992, and a day's count of that size could certainly be seen at the Sable Waters complex. Indeed, on this last-named group of pools, a walk around the perimeter of the two main lakes on 9th June 2003 produced a count of 240 adults just from the reeds that fringed the path; as the reed beds are quite extensive, only a small part of the area was covered and a very conservative estimate would have put the entire population on that day at over 1,000. On 12th July 2003, over 200 were seen in some 60 metres of ditch by the shore at Needs Ore Point at 07.30 hrs, mostly males, tandem pairs and pairs *in cop.* It was the beginning of a hot, sunny day, but two hours later the stretch of ditch contained only a score or so. The nearby habitat was saltmarsh and fields where cattle graze, and there did not seem to be any suitable habitat to which the damselflies would have moved. We have no counts from the Blackwater Valley, but populations along that stretch of river very probably equal some of those mentioned above.

FLIGHT PERIOD The Blue-tailed Damselfly has a long flight season, from early May (or even April) to late September. The Hampshire populations appear to be on the wing about ten days earlier than the dates given in the *Atlas of the Dragonflies of Britain and Ireland.*

EARLIEST/LATEST DATES Our earliest record is at Mortimer West End on 28th April 1995 and the latest near Eversley in the Blackwater Valley on 25th September 1990.

Male covered in early morning dew
© Cindy Allen

ADDITIONAL NOTES Females of this species are variable and exhibit five colour forms, some of which are immature colour forms, these being *violacea, infuscans, infuscans-obsoleta, rufescens* and normal, the last being similar to the male. All five varieties are present in the New Forest and some of the forms will be encountered in most of the large populations throughout the county.

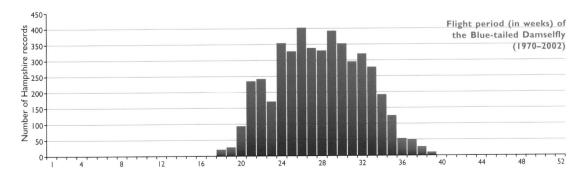

Flight period (in weeks) of
the Blue-tailed Damselfly
(1970–2002)

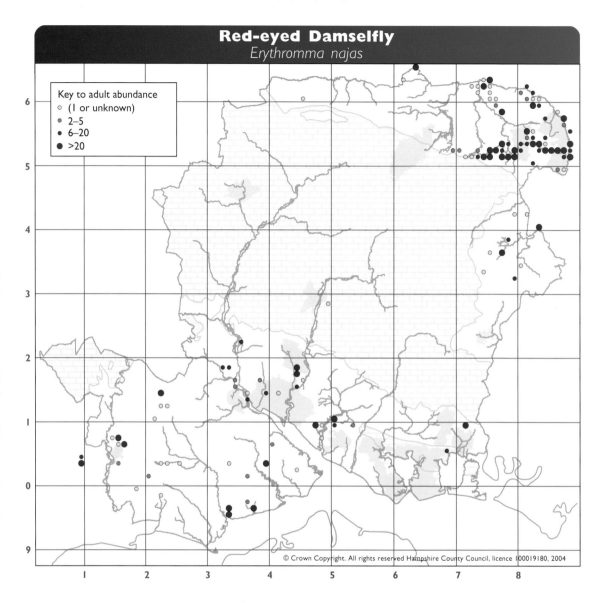

Red-eyed Damselfly
Erythromma najas

Key to adult abundance
- ○ (1 or unknown)
- ◦ 2–5
- ● 6–20
- ● >20

DISTRIBUTION The Red-eyed Damselfly is normally associated with mesotrophic lakes and the larger ponds and old water-filled quarries that have floating vegetation. Within Hampshire, this species is mainly found on the Tertiary rocks of the north and south, the former being the most important area with the Basingstoke Canal and its associated waters the real stronghold. There is also a scatter of occupied sites on the rocks of the Wealden anticline, but a complete absence from the chalk.

HABITAT The preferred habitat is one with plenty of aquatic vegetation that has large floating leaves, such as water lilies and broad-leaved pondweeds. Adults are frequently seen settled on these floating leaves, with territorial males guarding their leaves from all other damselfly species. With these habits, the Red-eyed Damselfly frequents the more open water areas of lakes and ponds whereas many other damselfly species prefer the margins and emergent vegetation. It does use the margins, but less so than other species, possibly because floating vegetation with broad leaves tends to grow on the more open water of a lake.

MAJOR LOCALITIES In and around the New Forest, Eyeworth Pond, Sable Pond, Bowman's Pond and the lakes in grounds of Walhampton School hold important populations, and this is almost certainly the position at some of the Blashford Lakes in the Avon valley above Ringwood, where further surveys are needed; Ivy Lake and Ellingham Lake are probably of particular importance there. Swanwick Nature Reserve is another of southern Hampshire's best sites, along with Staunton Country Park at Havant and Woodmill Salmon Ponds at Lakeside Country Park. Various stretches of the Basingstoke Canal, such as those at Poulters Bridge, are amongst the most favoured sites in the north of the county, along with Shortheath and Kingsley Ponds and parts of the Blackwater Valley.

POPULATION STRENGTHS At suitable locations with a quantity of well-established floating plants, it is not uncommon to see in excess of 20 individuals either patrolling the area of floating leaves or settled on them. At the best sites, over 100 individuals have been seen, such as at Swanwick Nature Reserve on 27th May 1992, Great Goswell Copse in August 1990 and the lakes at Hordle Walhampton School in August 2002. At this last locality, the population over the whole water area was almost certainly in excess of 100, and 52 were counted there on part of just one of the lakes on 20th July 2003. Sable Pond may also have counts reaching

three figures; over 50 have been seen on one day and further work at the site may well show this to be an under estimate of the true population. Yet another pond with a day's population that may approach or exceed 100 is Eyeworth Pond, and the same situation might well be found at the Blashford Gravel Pits. More census work on numbers needs to be carried out at waters such as Kingsley and Shortheath Ponds, whilst on the River Blackwater, several sites have had regular counts of over 100, although as with other species, the river is shared with Surrey and so the populations may not all be in Hampshire. A selection of large counts on the Basingstoke Canal is as follows: *ca.* 350 at Eelmoor Flash on 14th August 1998, and 250 at the same site

Male resting on vegetation © *Barry Hilling*

on 17th July 1996; 236 at Crookham Village on 9th June 1996 and 226 there on 4th July 1995; *ca.*150 in the Claycart Flash area on 14th August 1998 and 120 at East Coxmoor on 1st August 1995 (count by David and Jean Dell and Chris Hall). To give an idea of numbers on less important sites for the species, at Eelmoor Marsh a record count for the area was of 14 on 25th June 2001.

FLIGHT PERIOD In Hampshire, the species emerges in mid-May and its flight season extends to mid-September, with the latest records coming from the north of the county.

EARLIEST/LATEST DATES The Basingstoke Canal provides both the earliest and latest dates, these being at Claycart Flash on 8th May 1998 and on 22nd September 1994 respectively.

BEHAVIOUR Females oviposit in tandem in patches of floating and submerged vegetation and will sometimes completely submerge either with or without the male still attached.

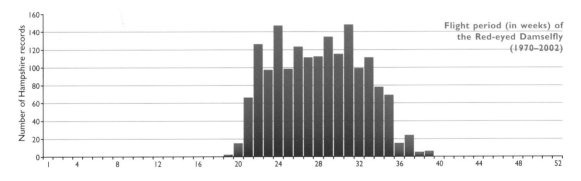

Flight period (in weeks) of
the Red-eyed Damselfly
(1970–2002)

Dragonflies *Anisoptera*

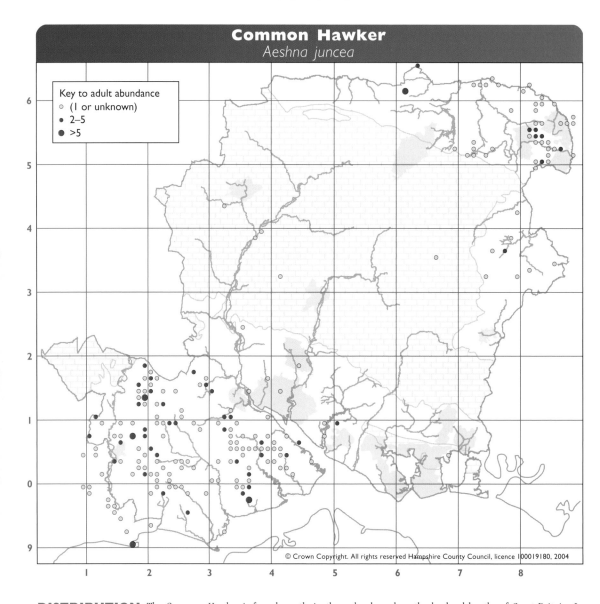

Common Hawker
Aeshna juncea

Key to adult abundance
- ○ (1 or unknown)
- • 2–5
- ● >5

DISTRIBUTION The Common Hawker is found mostly in the uplands and on the lowland heaths of Great Britain. In Hampshire, this species tends to be restricted to the heaths and ponds of the New Forest and to the north-east of the county, both in the Tertiary rocks and to a lesser extent in the rocks of the Wealden anticline, but in the well-watched area around the Basingstoke Canal, it is a rather scarce species. The adjective 'Common' is certainly misleading when applied to Hampshire, where the Southern Hawker is far more abundant and widespread and more deserving of the adjective 'Common'. There has been some confusion amongst observers between male Common and Migrant Hawkers, and in several localities such as Needs Ore and Sheepwash for example, the latter species is also more deserving of the name 'Common'.

HABITAT This Hawker is typically a moorland pond or peaty pool species, with patrolling males slowly hunting round the pond margins for accessible females. It is often to be found in association with other species, such as Black Darter, Four-spotted Chaser and Emerald Damselfly that are able to tolerate the acidic conditions of heathland pools. In common with most other Hawkers, this species can often be found feeding over heathland or along woodland rides well away from water and is one of the high-fliers of the dragonfly world, often seen overhead against the summer sky or perched high up in tall trees, tantalizingly out of camera reach.

Larvae tend to stay in the *Sphagnum* moss at pool edges during the first year and as they mature they seek shelter in the fringe vegetation. Emergence invariably takes place on tall emergent plants such as Common Cottongrass and rushes.

MAJOR LOCALITIES Despite this creature's vernacular name, it is not a widespread dragonfly in Hampshire. Amongst the more favoured sites are Shortheath Pond, Hundred Acre Piece at Mortimer, Woolmer, Broxhead and the Burley Old Railway Line.

POPULATION STRENGTHS This species is usually encountered in Hampshire in small numbers, with a sighting of two or more individuals at any one time being rather unusual. Males are not very tolerant of other males in their mating territory, which would account for such low numbers. However, more than six were seen flying in the Sheepwash area on 10th August 1993. A single male was holding territory on a private fishing lake alongside the River Test in 2000. A check on the same lake in August 2003 revealed three males aggressively competing for territory. Monitoring of lakes in the North-west of the county, including those in the Andover area, may result in further records.

There is a major risk of confusion between male Common Hawkers and fully adult male Migrant Hawkers for observers who are relatively inexperienced with dragonflies.

FLIGHT PERIOD The Common Hawker is a summer dragonfly and may be seen in June, although more commonly in July and August. With a good Indian Summer and an absence of early frosts, this Hawker may well be found on the wing in late October.

EARLIEST/LATEST DATES The species had a long flying season in 1993 with the last on 28th October at Swanwick Nature Reserve. However, the earliest was in 1998 when one was seen at Bourley Fir Hills on 14th June.

Pair in cop © Peter Allen

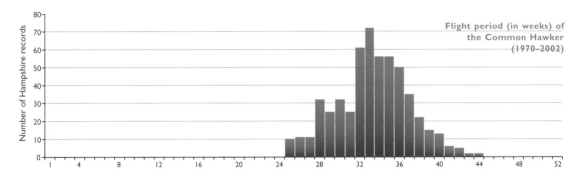

Flight period (in weeks) of the Common Hawker (1970–2002)

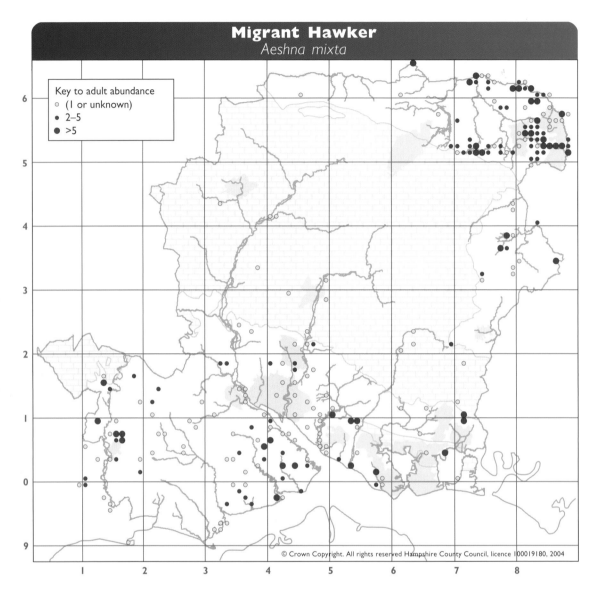

Migrant Hawker
Aeshna mixta

Key to adult abundance
- ○ (1 or unknown)
- • 2–5
- ● >5

DISTRIBUTION The map shows a heavy concentration in north-east Hampshire around the Basingstoke Canal and the Blackwater Valley, a fair sprinkling of records on the southern Tertiary rocks and a similar sprinkling on the Wealden rocks in the east of the county. Very few records have come from the chalk. As a species that appears to be increasing in Hampshire, it is possible that the southern Tertiaries will become more important for the species as it is there that the increase is perhaps most noticeable.

Records by Richards, Longfield and others for north-east Hampshire confirm it was a widespread and common breeding species there by the late 1930s. It was 'quite common' along much of the Basingstoke Canal in 1929 and the canal was one of the first sites in Britain where the species was proved to breed, albeit on the Surrey section (Longfield, 1949).

HABITAT This species favours well-vegetated pools and slow-flowing rivers and canals where it breeds at sites with lush emergent vegetation. The species will tolerate brackish waters and occupy other habitats. Gravel pits are used, along with drainage ditches and pools along the low-lying coastal marshes and pastures of Hampshire. Being a species that travels considerable distances, adults appear in a variety of habitats. It is less territorial than other Hawkers, with five to ten males sometimes occupying one pond together.

It has been stated that the Migrant Hawker avoids acidic pools, but no dragonfly in Britain avoids such waters. They are attracted by the habitat and the structure and nature of the vegetation. Research has shown that when acidic pools are limed and the *p*H altered, the same dragonfly species remain. The Migrant Hawker has weed-dwelling larvae that develop within the season after emerging from diapause, the ova frequently being laid in plant stems above summer water levels in anticipation of the rising water levels of winter.

MAJOR LOCALITIES Up to the mid-1990s, most of the major sites were in the north of the county at waters such as Shortheath Pond, Hook Common Pond and various sites along the Basingstoke Canal and the River Blackwater. In recent years, an increasing number of sites have been discovered in southern Hampshire with the nature reserves at Needs Ore and Titchfield Haven holding good populations, whilst the tiny pool at Sheepwash has been a most reliable site for seeing this species. The coastal belt seems to be particularly attractive to this species in autumn – at Needs Ore, for instance, Migrant Hawkers can be quite numerous, with at least 12 and possibly 20 around the Blackwater pools and paths on 25th September 2002, whilst at the Titchfield Haven Reserve, around 50 were recorded around the same date. The Avon Valley gravel pits have also held populations that would put them into the 'major locality' class.

Male at Needs Ore Point © *John Taverner*

POPULATION STRENGTHS It is not unusual to see over ten individuals flying together over the larger ponds and suitable stretches of canal. On two occasions, counts in excess of 20 adults were recorded, the first at King's Copse Inclosure on the 8th September 1991 and the second at Wellington Country Park on 17th September 1996. On 15th August 1994 20 adults were at Ash Embankment and similar counts have come from a few sites in the Blackwater Valley. Impressive numbers have been seen migrating in Europe and Hampshire has a similar example. Keith Lovegrove found 60 on the evening of 22nd August 2001 in reclaimed gravel pits away from water at Cadland Heath. The next day he counted 200 in 2 hours and seeing a similar density further on, estimated a possible count of 500, all of which appeared to be males. None was left on the 24th.

FLIGHT PERIOD In Hampshire, this species flies from late July into October and may be seen increasingly often in November. Most of the late-flying records have come from the north of the county, although as stated in a previous passage, autumn records from the coastal belt have become more numerous in the last few years.

EARLIEST/LATEST DATES The earliest record comes from Shave Wood in the New Forest, on 24th July 1988, whilst the latest record comes from Eelmoor Marsh on 28th November 1991. Although it has been seen just within the fence of Eelmoor Marsh, the dragonfly had obviously flown off the canal which is only 30 metres away.

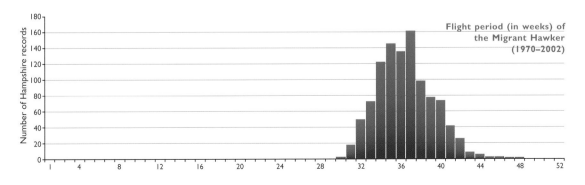

Flight period (in weeks) of the Migrant Hawker (1970–2002)

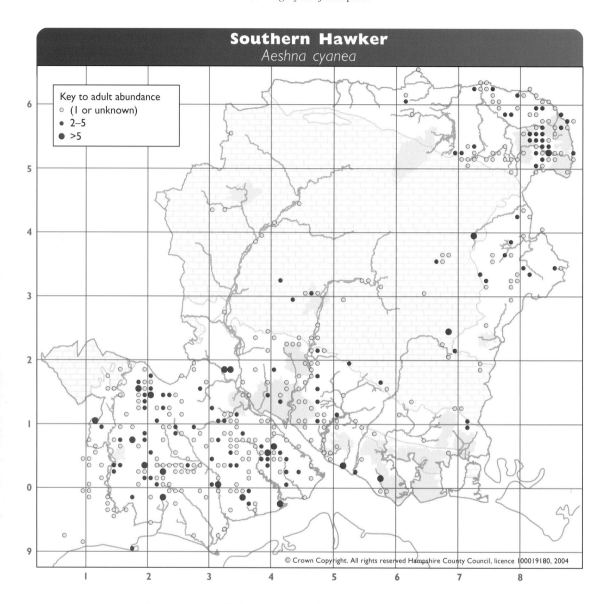

Southern Hawker
Aeshna cyanea

Key to adult abundance
- ○ (1 or unknown)
- • 2–5
- ● >5

DISTRIBUTION This is the most widely distributed Hawker in the county, and although the vast majority of records come from the Tertiary rocks, there is a good sprinkling of sightings from the Wealden anticline and from the chalk, these last sightings including breeding insects and individuals hunting or resting in a variety of sites such as woodland rides. On one occasion in 2000, an emergent was found on a tiny garden pond in Winchester on the high chalk, the pond in question being only eight feet across.

HABITAT A Hawker of ponds and still waters, this species is the 'proper' dragonfly recognised at many garden ponds. This Hawker is very inquisitive and will hover and inspect humans who enter its territory, whether that is at a breeding ground or at places well away from water. Males are aggressive and will intercept and drive off any intruding male that invades its territory. Territorial clashes are minimised by an apparently accidental time-sharing system whereby several males will visit and patrol at different times of day and so avoid conflict. Males may be frequently encountered hawking along the hedges and banks of country lanes and along rides in woodland, certain rides being used year after year whereas neighbouring rides that appear similar to human eyes are ignored. Mature males are often encountered in such localities by day or in the dimming light of summer evenings, often at a considerable distance from water at sites such as Crab Wood, about a mile out of Winchester on the high chalk and 145 metres above sea-level. Males at such sites will often patrol a territory, hunting back and forth along the same stretch and driving off other males that invade the space. Females are sometimes heard during ovipositing as they manoeuvre their wings against constricting vegetation. Ova are frequently laid in moss or soft soil above the water, although more conventional oviposition in submerged stems is also observed.

The larvae are to be found amongst submerged vegetation of ponds, pools and canals and the species has bred successfully in garden ponds on the chalk that are no more than two metres across.

MAJOR LOCALITIES The species is so widely distributed that there are too many sites that would deserve the title 'major' to list them all here, so the following is simply a selection taken from both north and south Hampshire. Furzey Pool, Ditch End Brook and the area around Sheepwash and East End Gravel Pit are such sites in the New Forest; the nature reserves at Titchfield

Haven and Needs Ore are coastal sites that would warrant inclusion in this category, whilst in the north of the county, Ancell's Farm near Fleet, Eelmoor Marsh and various other sites along the Basingstoke Canal would also qualify for such a list.

POPULATION STRENGTHS Numbers at any one site at the same time rarely exceed five. However, occasionally counts of up to 20 have been recorded such as at Ditch End Brook on 31st August 1991 and on the Basingstoke Canal at Claycart Flash on 21st August 1989. There have been records of quite sizeable emergences from very small garden ponds. Heather Tait sent in such records from her pond at Alton that has a surface area of just 4.5 square metres: at 13.30 hrs on 25th August 1997, 25 newly emerged specimens were seen there; in the following year, at least 20 exuvia were found during the last week of June, whilst in 2001, at least 30 emergents appeared between the 14th and 20th June. Another set of interesting figures comes from the small garden pond of Peter and Cindy Allen at North Gorley,

Adult male © *Cindy Allen*

near Fordingbridge. The pond was dug in 1992 and the following are numbers of exuvia per year: 1994, 53; 1995, 27; 1996, 78; 1997, 35; 1998, 88; 1999, 73; 2000, 119; 2001, 102; 2002, 95; 2003, 103. This total of 773 exuvia in just ten years from a small garden pond seems remarkable and demonstrates the importance of such habitat to this order of insects.

FLIGHT PERIOD In Hampshire, the species will be seen from June into November in most years. The vast majority of late records are of individuals seen in the south of the county.

EARLIEST/LATEST DATES Our earliest record comes from an emergent at the North Gorley garden pond mentioned in the text above, the date being 23rd May 1999, and the latest was in the New Forest at Rhinefield on 14th November 1990.

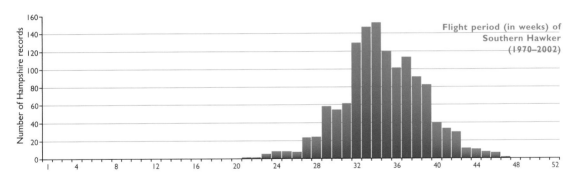

Flight period (in weeks) of
Southern Hawker
(1970–2002)

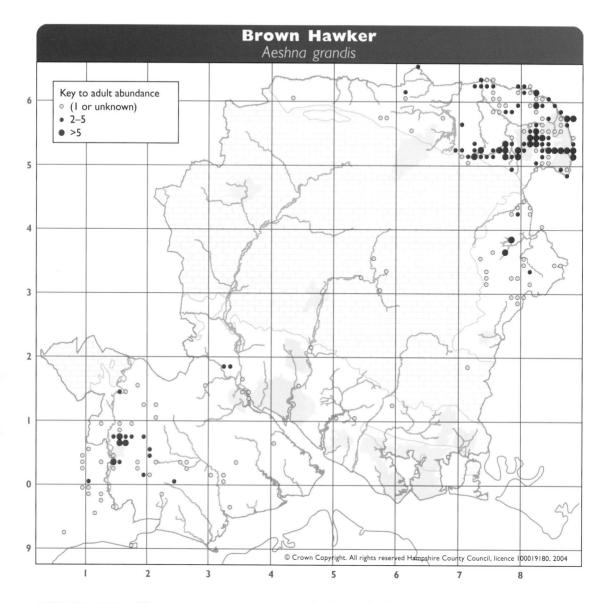

Brown Hawker
Aeshna grandis

Key to adult abundance
- ○ (1 or unknown)
- ● 2–5
- ● >5

DISTRIBUTION This Hawker has a somewhat local distribution in Hampshire because its required habitat is not so widespread as that needed by most of the other Hampshire Hawkers. Records from the chalk are few and far between, with the vast majority of records coming from the Tertiary rocks, especially those of north Hampshire. The above map shows very clearly the importance of the north-east, especially the Basingstoke Canal area, whilst the distribution in the New Forest and the southern Tertiaries is rather unusual, with a marked absence from much of the New Forest. This may be because some of the larger Forest pools, such as Hatchet Pond, lack suitable habitat to attract ovipositing females and have few trees around their margins, for the species has a habit of perching high in waterside trees; Sable Pond lies just outside the Forest boundary, on similar geology to the northern Forest, and with plenty of trees around the shore it is a good Brown Hawker site, with plenty of detritus around the shores for females to oviposit.

Although sightings of males have been recorded in the New Forest as far east as Tuckers Bridge Pond, where a female was seen ovipositing at the small tree-lined pond, the main breeding records have come from the extreme western edge of the Forest. Up to a dozen males may be seen hawking along the open woodland edges on either side of Linford Bottom in most years and oviposition has been recorded regularly at Water Slade Bottom Pond and once at Akercome Bottom Pond. These sites are within 4 km of

Poulner Lake. Breeding has also been recorded in the past at two commercial coarse fishing lakes near Burley, namely Beeches Brook and Turf Croft Farm, but it is uncertain whether or not the species occurs here naturally or was introduced with the fish stock. Over the last four years, males have been recorded even further to the south-east at a relatively new pond in Little Wootton Inclosure, and in 2003 a single female was seen ovipositing there. A single male was seen associating with Migrant and Southern Hawkers at the lake complex at Hordle Walhampton School in October 2003.

The larvae tend to inhabit waterside detritus, and it may also be the case that waters with many trees on the banks contain more leaf litter and so provide ideal larval habitat.

HABITAT This Hawker inhabits ponds and pools, especially those of reasonable size that are edged with trees, as well as stretches of the Basingstoke Canal and the Blackwater Valley, and it is quite tolerant of brackish waters. It moves into gravel pits once the margins are colonised by plants and is frequently seen over ornamental ponds in town parks. Like the Southern Hawker, it may be encountered in the evening twilight.

Larvae are to be found amongst the leaf litter, submerged vegetation and tree roots of pond, pool and canal.

MAJOR LOCALITIES Many of the better sites are in the north of the county at places such as Shortheath Pond, Kingsley Pond, Fleet Pond, Eversley Gravel Pits and parts of the Basingstoke Canal and River Blackwater. In the south, present data suggest that Linbrook Lake, Poulner Lake and Sable Pond are the best waters, whilst the Nature Reserve at Blashford Lakes may also hold a useful population. More work is needed at this last-named site.

Adult male at rest © *John Taverner*

POPULATION STRENGTHS At favoured sites, it is not unusual to find five or more individuals patrolling a pond and its surrounds. Records show a number of locations, including Fleet Pond and Linbrook Lake, where around ten adults were encountered, whilst exceptional counts in excess of 20 individuals were made at Ash Lock on the Basingstoke Canal on 25th July 1996 and at Poulner Lake on 16th July 1989.

FLIGHT PERIOD In Hampshire, this species flies from June through to November in mild years, with records indicating a later flight period in the north of the county..

EARLIEST/LATEST DATES The earliest date that has been recorded is the 18th June 1997 at Lakeside Park near Aldershot, with the latest on the Basingstoke Canal at Up Nately on 10th October 1993.

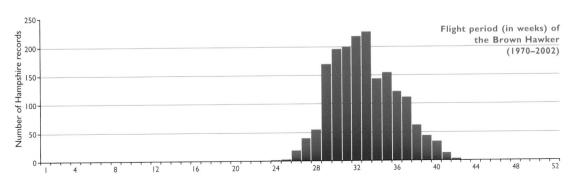

Flight period (in weeks) of the Brown Hawker (1970–2002)

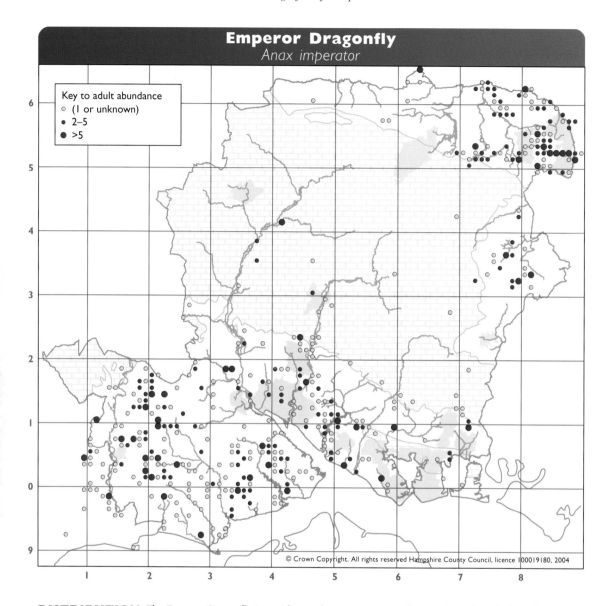

Emperor Dragonfly
Anax imperator

Key to adult abundance
- ○ (1 or unknown)
- • 2–5
- ● >5

DISTRIBUTION The Emperor Dragonfly is a widespread species in areas of Hampshire where bodies of still water occur. It is found on all the larger ponds in the New Forest and in the heathland districts of the north and east, where it frequents pools and ponds. It also occurs at many parts of the Basingstoke Canal, on gravel-pit lakes in the Blackwater Valley, and is sometimes encountered hunting over heathland well away from water. Males will hold a territory on much smaller pools, even on the chalk; a male soon took up territory on a new but small dew-pond that was constructed on chalk downland at the top of Stockbridge Down, driving off other males that appeared and mating with a female which oviposited in the pool.

HABITAT The main habitat for this Hawker is still waters of varying sizes, with no connection to pH values. Smaller ponds will support no more than one male territory at any one time, but larger water bodies often carry a number of territorial males. Like all Hawkers, the Emperor is a strong flier, spending long periods patrolling territory. It is perhaps seen more often over water than the related *Aeshna* species

MAJOR LOCALITIES All major sites are away from the chalk, although as the previous text has stated, the species does inhabit man-made waters on the chalk. It can be seen on most lakes and larger ponds on other rock types, and a few examples of waters where there is a strong population are the Sable Waters complex of pools, Exbury Garden pools, East End Gravel Pit and nearby Sheepwash, to name but a few of many. It also occurs throughout the Blackwater Valley catchment area.

POPULATION STRENGTHS In the summers of 2001 and 2003, a dozen males were on Sable Pond and its surrounding system of smaller ponds and pools at the same time, the whole area covering an area of perhaps four or five football pitches. This would be a very strong population for such a large species whose males do not tolerate other males in their territory. Even the best localities will probably produce counts of males in low single figures at any one time, due to this intolerance of competitors of their own species. It is therefore very difficult to estimate the size of a population because as one male takes a rest from patrolling a territory, another will take over. In an area such as Exbury Gardens, with its complex of man-made pools, a walk on 14th July 2003 produced over 20 individuals and this would have been the proverbial tip of an iceberg, whilst a walk beside the Basingstoke Canal in peak season should produce a count of 20 or more, though bridge-to-bridge sections rarely hold more than three at one time. Exceptionally, 12 were in the Claycart area on 8th July 1995 and 13 were at nearby Eelmoor Marsh, where there are over 30 pools, on 12th June 2003.

Immature after emergence © *John Taverner*

FLIGHT PERIOD This is an early species, one of the first of the large Hawkers to appear. It is the origin of the term "Spring Species" as described by Corbet (1954) in his study of synchronised emergence in some species of dragonfly. This study was undertaken at Wokefield Common in Berkshire. It is on the wing in Hampshire from the third week in May through to mid-September with the earlier records tending to come from the south of the county.

EARLIEST/LATEST DATES The earliest record is on 20th May 1990 at Furzey Pool in the New Forest, whilst the latest is on 20th September 1989 on the Basingstoke Canal at Claycart Flash.

ADDITIONAL NOTES On 20th July 2003, Alan Hold and John Taverner watched an unusual female ovipositing in Hatchet Pond. The insect was an elderly female with tattered wings that were no longer clear and transparent but brown and a little opaque. The colour of the abdomen was a clear blue, as blue as any adult male Emperor at its best with no sign of green, and the insect was watched for some ten minutes or so as it oviposited continually around a small pool. In some species, elderly females take on male coloration, but this individual had the abdomen of a perfect male Emperor.

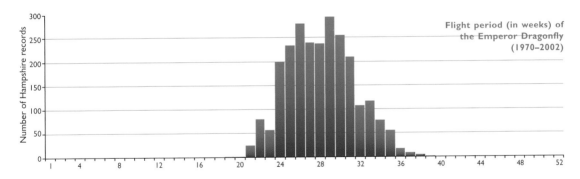

Flight period (in weeks) of the Emperor Dragonfly (1970–2002)

Number of Hampshire records

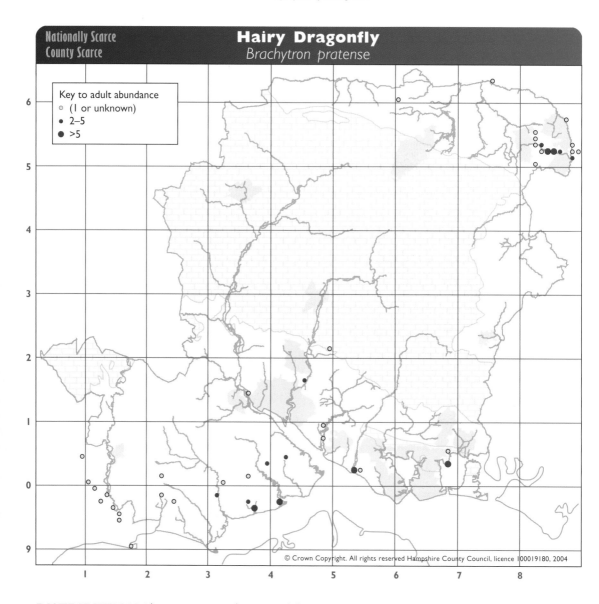

Nationally Scarce
County Scarce

Hairy Dragonfly
Brachytron pratense

Key to adult abundance
○ (1 or unknown)
• 2–5
● >5

DISTRIBUTION The species seems to have expanded its range in Hampshire over the past two decades and this would appear to be a true expansion and not simply due to more extensive coverage of the county by observers. This statement is supported by a similar increase in other counties in southern England. During the Key Sites Project (1988–1993) the species was recorded at just six sites in Hampshire, but since the late 1990s it is found breeding at a number of sites, two of which are on the coast, and this coastal strip appears to be the Hairy Dragonfly's stronghold in southern Hampshire. Needs Ore and Titchfield Haven are the two key sites and are possibly centres from which the species can penetrate inland.

The other centre is in north-east Hampshire along the Basingstoke Canal. Here the Hairy Dragonfly has been known for over 60 years (Hall 1993, quoting Richards) and has been recorded regularly from most parts east of Fleet to the county boundary. In 1998 there were records for the first time from Eelmoor Marsh, an SSSI adjacent to the canal near Farnborough and the species

Female at coastal colony © *John Taverner* ➤

has been recorded there in low numbers in every subsequent year. It has also been recorded regularly since the 1990s from gravel pit lakes in the Blackwater Valley.

HABITAT At Needs Ore, this species' preferred habitat is along a ditch beside Blackwater that contains tall reeds with patches of open water, the males patrolling an open path beside the ditch that is bordered on the other side by a bank with conifers and the large brackish pool of Blackwater. By 2003, the ditch had become overgrown and special management to keep parts open is essential if it is to remain prime habitat for this species. At the same location, the species also frequents an area very close to the shore where an open grassy area with much Bramble and Gorse contains small pools. At Titchfield Haven, the ditches alongside a path leading to the Pumfret and Spurgin hides, and the pool at Darter's Dip, are managed with dragonflies in mind and rotational

clearing of ditches providing both open water and tall marginal vegetation create the preferred habitat for Hairy Dragonflies. The management scheme at Titchfield Haven permits a slow flow of water along these ditches throughout the year, although at times the flow is hardly perceptible. Along with Needs Ore, this is probably the best site to see male Hairy Dragonflies holding territory and patrolling ditches, about a metre above the water, seeking the more secretive females and it is possible to see the females ovipositing into the submerged plants along the margins of the ditch.

No studies have been undertaken to determine the habitat preferences of this species on the Basingstoke Canal, though monitoring for eleven years up to 2000 showed a strong association with the heathland zone. Studies of this species at gravel pit lakes in the Blackwater Valley have concluded that the Hairy Dragonfly is selective not only in its choice of waterbody but also on the sections of lake margin it will utilise for breeding. Sites favoured were those with a good cover and variety of submerged and emergent vegetation in bays with shallow water. The species is unlikely to be found at sites with

Adult male at a Hampshire coastal colony © *John Taverner*

few wetland plants, where scrub grows out into shallow water or where the banks are bare (Bailey, 1997; Parkinson, 1993). At Eelmoor Marsh, the Hairy Dragonfly is usually seen over well-vegetated ditches in which the water is shallow and slow flowing – much like the conditions on the coastal sites at Needs Ore and Titchfield Haven.

MAJOR LOCALITIES Needs Ore and Titchfield Haven nature reserves have already been picked out as two main localities, whilst Middle Pond on the Beaulieu Estate has also held good numbers, along with Toby's Pond in Botley Wood and Farlington Marshes. In the north-east, many records have come from the Basingstoke Canal and since 1990 new habitats close to the canal have been colonised.

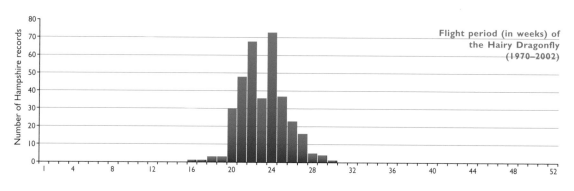

Flight period (in weeks) of
the Hairy Dragonfly
(1970–2002)

POPULATION STRENGTHS At the Needs Ore site beside the reed-choked ditch, up to five males have been seen flying at the same time along the length of the bordering path, which is around 150 metres in length. This would be a strong population for Hampshire, but it is not known whether other males are nearby or if the five patrolling form the bulk of the population for that particular patch. They seem to keep to their particular beat and other males on the nearby shore would seem to be different individuals, so that at Needs Ore at one time there may be around ten flying males. At Titchfield Haven, numbers seem similar to those at Needs Ore; a search of all suitable sites on the Reserve at Titchfield Haven produced one male on 28th April, four males and three females on 11th May, and 21 males and nine females on 18th May. In 2003, a count at the lower end of Titchfield Haven produced ten males and three females. Counts on sections of the Basingstoke Canal are usually of only one or two adults, but occasionally five or more have been reported at Farnborough and Ash Embankment.

FLIGHT PERIOD The Hairy Dragonfly is often the first of the Anisoptera to appear, usually at the beginning of May with a flight period that normally extends to early July.

EARLIEST/LATEST DATES The earliest record was on 28th April 1998 at Titchfield Haven, followed by records on the first day of May in 1993 and 1997 on the Basingstoke Canal at Ash Embankment. The latest date is also from the Basingstoke Canal, at Norris Bridge on 15th July 1991.

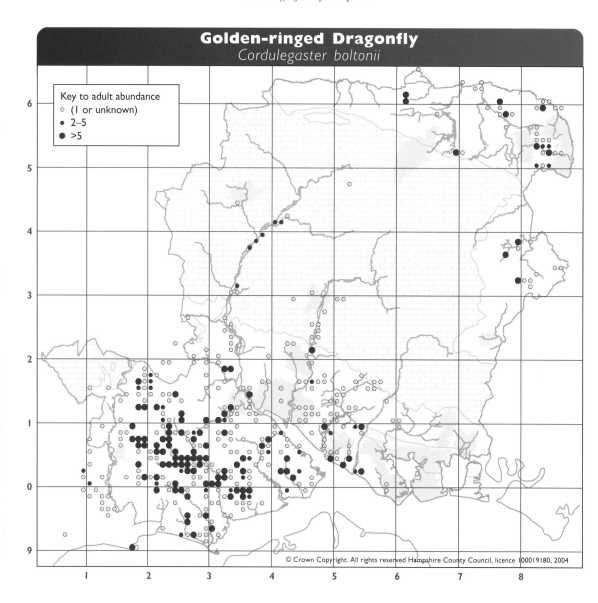

Golden-ringed Dragonfly
Cordulegaster boltonii

Key to adult abundance
- ○ (1 or unknown)
- • 2–5
- ● >5

DISTRIBUTION In Hampshire, this species is found breeding mostly at habitats on the rocks to the south and north of the chalk, being especially numerous in the New Forest, which is the species' stronghold in the county and where most streams hold reasonable numbers. It ranges widely across the heaths of northern Hampshire, the Warren Heath streams being a good example, and it may well breed in small numbers in isolated ditches over a large area of north-east Hampshire. Larvae have been found by Environment Agency workers at a handful of localities in the Wealden rocks and at a number of sites south of the chalk but away from the New Forest, the upper tributary valleys of the River Hamble showing quite a cluster of such records in their small runners and ditches. This search for larvae by the Environment Agency has also produced evidence of breeding on the chalk. During the past decade, Agency field workers have found larvae at a few sites in the chalk reaches of the Rivers Test and Itchen, so that the chalkland sightings mentioned in the following paragraph may have involved some breeding insects and not simply adults that had moved away from breeding grounds to feed or allow wings to fully harden after hatching, which was thought to be the case when Golden-ringed Dragonflies were found in such habitat. Examples of larvae found by Environment Agency field workers in chalk stretches of both the Itchen and

Adult female © *Peter Allen*

the Test systems are: ***River Test valley:*** Kimbridge, 13th April 1995; Awbridge House, 22nd April, 1992, 5th May 1999 and 16th October 2002; Awbridge Farm, 30th September 2002; Horsebridge, 19th October 1995; Kings Somborne area, 22nd October 2001, 21st January 2002 and 22nd April 2002. ***River Itchen valley:*** Twyford waterworks; 9th October 1991 and 8th April 1992; Compton Lock, 7th May 2002; Mariner's Meadow, 5th February 2002. There have also been records from the ***River Meon*** at Mislingford Weir. Compared with Hampshire's other geological areas, these larval records from the chalk are minimal, but they are of great importance because the national dragonfly database does not hold any other such records from the chalk.

When not in breeding territory, the species has been found in most areas, even on the dry chalklands where there have been a handful of records, although as with chalk larval finds, such records are very small in number when compared with heathland areas. Examples on the chalk hills around Winchester of sightings of adults that were not in breeding habitat are of a female found eating a large bee on a grass-covered reservoir on the city's northern outskirts, a male patrolling a woodland ride on the southern outskirts of the city, and a male that stayed for most of a day in a garden situated well within the city's suburbs. Sightings of adults along the chalk rivers did occur in suitable breeding habitat, such as two males that were resting in bushes at Chilbolton Water-meadows, just a few metres from the River Test, but before the Environment Agency's larval records came to light, these were thought to be adults that had moved there to feed. Similarly, Graham Vick recorded four males along the River Test at Wherwell during a Caddis Fly survey in 2002 and concluded that the species was possibly breeding on the silty channels rather than the main fly-fishing beats (see above paragraph). This species is regularly seen patrolling sections of the Longstock Water Gardens and the well-vegetated side runners of the Test, such as Parson's Stream at Longstock. Where suitable habitat exists, the Golden-ringed Dragonfly can be said to be reasonably common in Hampshire and during the period covered by this book, has produced records in almost a hundred of the county's one-kilometre squares.

Side view of resting male © *John Taverner*

HABITAT Larval areas are generally small heathland streams where the acidic water is shallow and the bed of the stream composed of silt or gravel, the streams usually slow-flowing because of their size and the gentle relief of the land through which they flow. Larval sampling along the Ober Water during March 1992 revealed that larvae of different instars were concentrated in areas with fine sandy patches. These streams are typically a metre or less in width and in one case, a well-used stream was no more than 30 cm wide with very shallow water. The stream banks often have quite lush vegetation, although in the case of the narrow stream mentioned in the previous sentence, the banks were bare clay because the ditch had only been created recently by a JCB. Vegetation on the banks of the streams may vary considerably, from overhanging trees to heather moorland; along the upper Crockford Stream, for instance, males patrol a stretch which flows from open heath through a narrow cutting that is lined with woodland and scrub, whilst along Latchmore Brook the species also breeds along a stretch of stream with similar changes in the surrounding vegetation. On the chalk, the breeding sites have been in small runners and ditches away from the main channel.

In such habitat, the vast majority of sightings are of males. Females of most *Anisoptera* come to water mainly to oviposit, and are seen in such habitat far less often than are males, but such appearances by female Golden-ringed Dragonflies seem particularly brief. Males, on the other hand, constantly patrol a regular beat in suitable areas in search of females.

Lakes, ponds and large rivers do not provide suitable breeding habitat, the first two of the trio just mentioned because the species needs flowing water and the last because the species shuns breeding areas in rivers where the flow of water is too great in either speed or volume.

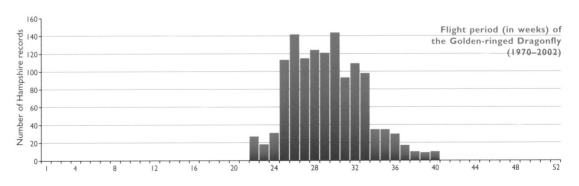

Flight period (in weeks) of the Golden-ringed Dragonfly (1970–2002)

MAJOR LOCALITIES Within the New Forest, the two streams named in the previous paragraph are but two well-known localities, and it has already been stated that most of the Forest streams have good populations, whilst a short way outside the Forest perambulation, private land at Sable Waters has small ditches that have been cut especially for dragonflies that also hold good numbers of Golden-ringed Dragonflies.

POPULATION STRENGTHS Five males were patrolling a stretch of stream no more than fifty metres in length at Embley Wood, whilst at the upper reaches of Crockford Stream, as many as eight males have been estimated to be simultaneously holding territories along a 200 metre stretch of stream. Similar counts have been made along Latchmore Brook. Nine were present along the ditch network of Eelmoor Marsh on 26th June 1999. Such numbers in Hampshire would represent strong populations.

FLIGHT PERIOD This species has a lengthy flight period in the county. Adults may be seen from late May until September, with peak activity probably being in July.

EARLIEST/LATEST DATES This species had a long flying season in 1992, with the first record on 25th May at Avon Water and the last on 20th September at Wellington Country Park. However, our latest date is 25th September 2003 at Lower Peaked Hill

BEHAVIOUR Males will patrol a territory along a stretch of stream. Where two territories meet there are regular clashes, the two males spiralling into the air before breaking off and resuming patrols of their respective beats. Females typically oviposit by selecting a shallow stream with a fine sandy or gravel bed. At these sites, they hover by flying vertically up and down whilst stabbing ova into the substrate with their lance shaped ovipositor. This is the only species in the UK that exhibits this form of ovipositing behaviour.

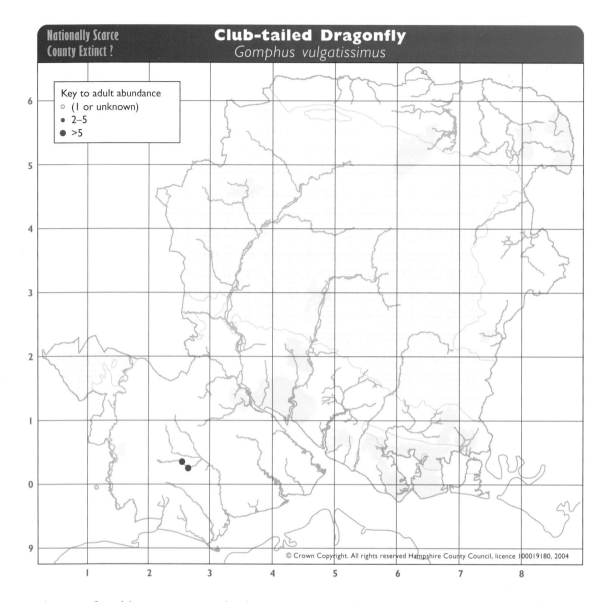

**Nationally Scarce
County Extinct ?**

Club-tailed Dragonfly
Gomphus vulgatissimus

Key to adult abundance
○ (1 or unknown)
● 2–5
● >5

The Dragonflies of the New Forest states that the species "…was abundant on the Ober Water, in early spring, during the 1930s and 1940s. Populations have gradually declined since that period and recent surveys have failed to locate this species in the New Forest." (Welstead, N & T, 1984). This was noted in the previous section on the White-legged Damselfly which has suffered a somewhat similar decline and this demise of the Club-tailed Dragonfly in the New Forest may be due to human influence, especially our removal of bankside vegetation and the introduction of livestock to the stream banks. However, this is not known for certain. It also occurred along part of the Moors River, which is now in Dorset. It is just possible that this species still exists in the county in very small numbers.

The species was never widespread in Hampshire, the only recorded sites being in the New Forest and the extreme south-west of the county, until in 1988 Lee Summersby reported it from Mortimer West End. The first county record is from J.C. Dale, at Parley Heath in 1872, but Lucas (1900) records it merely as "Hampshire: New Forest" and this is the only description of its occurrence (variously by Wainwright, Ashdown and Morton up to that date). In the years following the publication of Lucas' book, several observers recorded the species from Brockenhurst, but with no detail of the precise site. As the Ober

Water runs from the Markway Bridge section on to Brockenhurst, these records also probably refer to this section. By the time of Killington (1926) it is described as "a rare dragonfly only recorded, so far, from the south-west of the county, but quite likely to occur elsewhere". Although there are a number of apparently suitable riverine sites in Hampshire, Killington's optimism was unfounded; all records came from a handful of sites. There is an anonymous record from Avon Water, in the New Forest, from 1930; F.H. Haines and his daughter Gladys, both experienced and reliable observers, recorded it near their Linwood home, near Fordingbridge, between 1927 and 1940, and there were occasional reports from Hurn (presumably the Moors River) during the 1940s and early 1950s by F.D. Buck and F.C. Fraser. In 1950, Fraser claimed that "although the species occurs in several parts of the Thames Valley, its true home is the New Forest where, in the course of a morning's walk, more specimens may be seen than the total records for other localities". What days! Then, in 1959, Don Tagg recalls finding up to 38 exuviae along the Ober Water upstream of Puttles Bridge.

Maturing male © Peter Allen

Fraser's last records are from Hurn and Parley Heath, both south-west of the New Forest, in 1952 and 1958, and Keith Goodyear records finding a number of exuviae on the Ober Water near Rhinefield in May and June 1965, but despite a number of intensive searches, the species has not been seen since June 1970 when C.F. Cowan recorded it for the last time at its classic Ober Water site. The 1988 Summersby record was for one day and has not been repeated. However, exuvia cases were found on the Hampshire/Berkshire border at Thatcher's Ford by Steve Bailey and his team, an adult was seen flying there in the same season on the Hampshire side of the river, and Chris Hall has drawn our attention to three records on the River Blackwater in the period 1990–96.

At the time of writing, we must therefore consider the species as possibly lost to Hampshire, but the exuvia cases mentioned above suggest that a small population may still exist in that area, despite the lack of adult sightings on the River Blackwater. The species is quick to disperse from the breeding site and even at sites with strong populations in other counties, adult sightings can be very infrequent. Careful systematic searches are called for to see if a remnant population is still extant in the county. The nearest stronghold to Hampshire is along the River Thames in Oxfordshire and Berkshire. It is gradually moving down the tributaries, such as the River Loddon into new areas. Along one stretch of the Loddon in Berkshire, exuvia have been found on the mown lawn of a back garden bordering the river following a successful emergence. Only one flying adult has been reported from this site and highlights the need for careful observation of potential breeding areas.

BEHAVIOUR Following emergence, the Club-tailed Dragonfly disperses into woodland away from water. Immature adults have been recorded up to 10 km away from the nearest known breeding site. Most observers first encounter this species at the emergence site and searching these areas often reveals the characteristic exuvia.

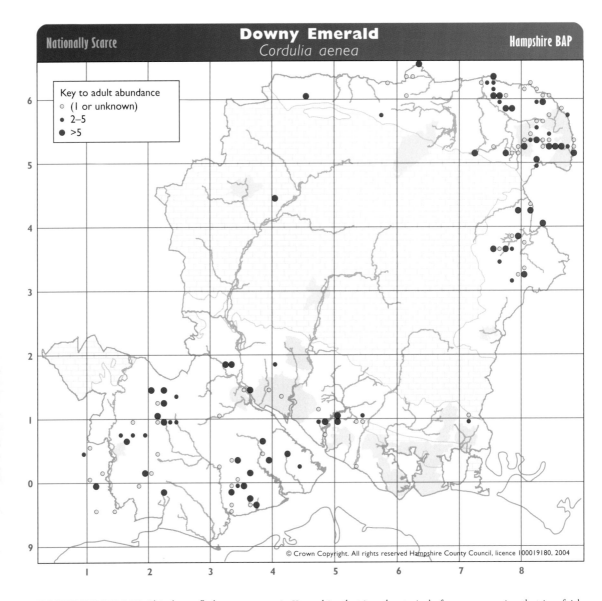

Downy Emerald
Cordulia aenea

Nationally Scarce

Hampshire BAP

Key to adult abundance
○ (1 or unknown)
● 2–5
● >5

DISTRIBUTION This dragonfly has a presence in Hampshire that is rather typical of so many species, that is a fairly widespread distribution in the New Forest and in the north-east of the county, with a thin scattering over parts of the Wealden rocks and a complete absence from the high chalk.

At this point, it may be useful to mention an area of nearby Berkshire that is an important Downy Emerald site, since this population could spread into Hampshire. An area spanning the Hampshire/Berkshire border between Mortimer and Aldermaston supports a significant population of Downy Emeralds. At one dammed pool just inside Berkshire, hundreds of Downy Emerald larvae have been measured as part of a study into the species' ecology. During the summer, large numbers emerge from this pond and utilise the extensive woodland for feeding. Work at this site has shown that larvae move into deeper water in winter, returning to the margins in early spring. Again, the larvae are concentrated in areas with slowly decomposing leaf litter and the main breeding site lies within 1 km of the Hampshire border.

Early morning immature with brown eyes © *Graham Sutton* ➤

HABITAT This species tends to be associated with ponds, lakes or canal sites with trees that overhang or are close to the water. Recent work has shown that larvae are found where there is slowly decomposing vegetation, such as leaf litter. If the pools and ponds are cleared of such material, the larvae cannot survive and so too much tidying up of a pool will make it unsuitable for the Downy Emerald. This would explain why at Sable Pond the species is only found around the older parts of the area where the banks have not been cleared for some time, whereas in the newer parts of the complex the species is not seen.

Dipping at Broomy Pond on 19th April 1997 demonstrated a clear separation between the larvae of the Downy Emerald and larvae of Four-spotted Chasers, the latter being associated with finer and more fibrous debris. Downy Emerald larvae were concentrated along the tree-lined margin of the pond where adults are mostly seen during the summer. Larvae of two very distinct size classes are found. The smaller sizes (7–13 mm) would not emerge during that year. Work at other sites

Immature with milky wings © Barry Hilling

has shown that early instar larvae are rarely found and these results would suggest that the species has a three year life cycle in the New Forest.

Compared to most other sites in southern England, the New Forest sites are atypical. Broomy and Hatchet Ponds, for example, are exposed with no woodland in the immediate vicinity. On the other hand, Sable Waters, which lie just outside the New Forest perambulation, contain typical Downy Emerald areas, and the same can be said of Toby's Pond in the Tertiaries near Wickham.

MAJOR LOCALITIES In the New Forest, important sites include Sheepwash Pond, Broomy Pond, East End Gravel Pit, Hatchet Pond, Eyeworth Pond, Bowman's Pond and Slufters Pond. Just outside the New Forest perambulation, Sable Pond also has reasonable numbers, whilst to the east of Southampton Water in the south of the county, Swanwick Nature Reserve and Toby's Pond, plus other smaller ponds, in Botley Wood also have healthy populations. In the north of the county, the species can be encountered at Warren Heath, Hundred Acre Piece (especially Oval Pond), Bourley Ponds, Yateley Common, Kingsley Pond, Woolmer, Liphook, Shortheath Pond and at several sites along the River Blackwater and the Basingstoke Canal. At this last-named locality, the stretch from Norris Hill to Aldershot is certainly a major locality. For several years during the 1990s, this species was recorded on the main pond at Hilliers' Arboretum, near Romsey. A closer check of tree-lined lakes and pools in mid-Hampshire may reveal additional sites.

POPULATION STRENGTHS A typical visit to one of the best sites would produce single figure counts of patrolling males, seldom with more than two or three in sight at the same time. As males are not very tolerant of one another, this is not

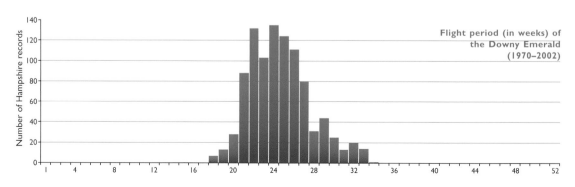

Flight period (in weeks) of
the Downy Emerald
(1970–2002)

Number of Hampshire records

surprising but it makes any assessment of population size almost impossible without some system of marking and capture, a fact that applies to most dragonfly species. Some of the highest counts have been 13 males at Toby's Pond, Botley Wood, on 14th June 2000, 12 in the Claycart area of the Basingstoke Canal on 30th June 2001, nine in the same area on 31st May 1997, eight on 18th June 1995 at Shortheath Pond, a similar number at the Claycart area again on 18th June 2000 and seven at Wyndham's Pond on 19th June 2001, and these counts, all by David and Jean Dell, would be excellent for Hampshire.

FLIGHT PERIOD The Downy Emerald is an early summer dragonfly, emerging at the beginning of May with adults encountered until the beginning of August. The peak season is in June, with the later records coming from the north of the county.

EARLIEST/LATEST DATES The north of the county provides both the earliest and latest dates. The earliest was on 5th May 1998 at Wyndham's Pond, Yateley, with other early sightings on 11th May 1999 at Ash Embankment, 14th May 1997 at Shortheath Pond, 15th May 1990 at Eelmoor Marsh and 15th May 1994 at Ash Embankment. The latest date that we have came from the Basingstoke Canal, at Claycart Flash on 31st August 1991. At one of the ponds along the Hampshire/ Berkshire border, an exuvia was found on 4th May 1997, whilst at Decoy Heath Pond, only a few hundred metres from the Hampshire border, a male was seen flying on 6th May. Emergence is usually synchronised over a short period and the population of this Berkshire area is usually on the wing by mid-May. It can sometimes be over a week before the first mature males are seen holding territories at the breeding sites.

BEHAVIOUR Studies of this species have shown that males occupying territories around a pool are in fact time-sharing with other males (Brook *et al.*, 1997). A male will vigorously defend a territory for 20–30 minutes before leaving the water, whereupon another male will move in and take the territory. Unique markings on the wings of adult males have shown that the few individuals seen at any one time often comprise but a small proportion of individuals that appear during the course of a day. The study also revealed that the current holder always wins when another male tries to take over. During other times, they utilise woodland rides in which to feed.

Females are most often encountered when they come to water to oviposit. They spend much of this time covertly flying close to the banks in order to avoid the attention of males. At Hundred Acre Piece, near Mortimer (Berkshire) a female was observed ovipositing over open water at 07.30 hrs on 16th June 1996 before males had arrived at the pond. This avoidance behaviour enables females to oviposit with lower risk of being intercepted.

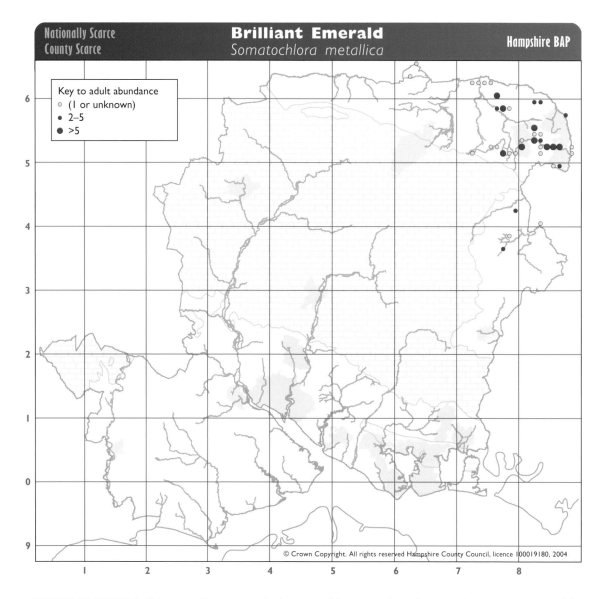

Nationally Scarce
County Scarce

Brilliant Emerald
Somatochlora metallica

Hampshire BAP

Key to adult abundance
○ (1 or unknown)
• 2–5
● >5

DISTRIBUTION This nationally scarce species has two widely separated populations in Britain, in one area of the Scottish Highlands and in part of south-east England that extends into north-east Hampshire. In the last-named area, it occurs over a wide area, almost exclusively within the heathland zone, in the vicinity of suitable breeding waters. Exceptionally, there have been a few records associated with the Basingstoke Canal at Coxmoor Wood, Odiham Common and Dogmersfield Park, almost into chalk country. Within the Thames Basin heathlands the Brilliant Emerald occurs widely, often utilising old, flooded gravel pits from Wellington Country Park, Warren Heath and Yateley Common in the north (where it extends its range into Berkshire) to the Basingstoke Canal, where it can be seen almost anywhere between Fleet and the county boundary at Aldershot. Indeed, it ranges well into Surrey along the Canal corridor. It has also been reported at a number of gravel pit lakes adjacent to the River Blackwater, and occasionally over the river itself. Over a period of 20 years there have been records from 14 ponds or lakes in this region of Hampshire, such as Shortheath and Kingsley Ponds, but because most are sites that are not monitored regularly, it is not known how many of these were casual occurrences.

Adult male © *Steve Cham*

Along the Berkshire border between Mortimer and Aldermaston, there is a significant population that utilises a series of lakes and ponds in the extensive woodland in this area. It is regularly recorded from Kiln Pond in Benyons Enclosure as well as smaller nearby pools. Males are great wanderers, often searching out new pools by flying along woodland rides and these metapopulations interact with each other. Individuals have been recorded at most of the pools in the area but at one series of pools to the north of Aldermaston, three males were observed holding territory at one pond. They had spaced themselves out to occupy equal portions of the water's surface. At the same time, Downy Emerald males were also present.

In East Hampshire the Brilliant Emerald is much more restricted, with records coming from Shortheath Pond, Kingsley Common and Alice Holt.

To the Victorian entomologists the Brilliant Emerald was exclusively a Scottish species (Follett, 1996), but by the 1940s it had been recognised at a number of sites in the South-east, including the Basingstoke Canal in both Surrey and Hampshire. A.W. Richards knew it from the Basingstoke Canal (Aldershot and elsewhere) in 1938 and at Fleet Pond in 1939 (Richards, 1941).

HABITAT The ecology of the Brilliant Emerald is poorly understood. It is associated with ponds, lakes and the Basingstoke Canal where the water is neutral or mildly acidic, in wooded areas where at least part of the margins of the waterbody are shaded and overhung, a feature that appears to be an essential character of the habitat. There seems to be no preference for either deciduous or coniferous woodland. Females in particular are often reported away from water, such as in rides through forestry plantations. A.W. Richards was shown a female in 1940 that had been "captured by a boy in a Farnborough street" (Richards, 1941), a feat that would be highly improbable today.

Larval sampling at a series of pools at Warren Heath revealed the larvae of the Brilliant Emerald to be less numerous than those of the Downy Emerald. The latter were found in reasonable numbers at all the pools, whereas Brilliant Emerald larvae were found only at the middle pool that is heavily shaded.

Adult male © *Peter Allen*

MAJOR LOCALITIES The Basingstoke Canal has long been regarded as the best site to see the Brilliant Emerald in Hampshire, though in recent years numbers have decreased. The above text states that a significant population also exists along the Hampshire/Berkshire border, and although the major breeding sites are just within Berkshire, individuals can be seen at several pools on the Hampshire side. Elsewhere it is fairly scarce, with few records.

POPULATION STRENGTHS As with most dragonflies, population estimates based on adult insects are unreliable because they disperse quickly after emergence. No detailed surveys of larvae or exuviae are available for any sites. Many records of adults are of one or two insects and only the detailed work of David and Jean Dell monitoring the Basingstoke Canal has produced higher counts. Their best counts for a section of canal have been eight in the Rushmoor Flash area on 9th August 1998 and ten in the vicinity of Claycart Bridge on 8th August 1997. Typical counts for the Fleet to Aldershot length of the canal (some 6 km) during the 1990s suggest that perhaps 15–20 might be present over the waterway in peak season.

FLIGHT PERIOD Emergence usually occurs in early June, some three weeks later than the Downy Emerald, though in advanced seasons an occasional record is made in May. The main flight period lasts until mid-August, but a very few may linger until the end of the month or very early September.

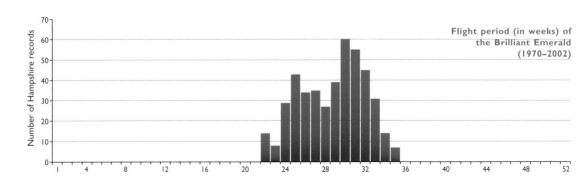

Flight period (in weeks) of the Brilliant Emerald (1970–2002)

EARLIEST/LATEST DATES Shortheath Pond provides the earliest record, that being on 23rd May 1993, but May records are rare. The latest modern record comes from Claycart Flash on the Basingstoke Canal, on the 31st August 1991, but A.W. Richards saw "several" over the canal on 2nd September 1939 (Richards, 1940). [The latest on the Surrey part of the canal was on 14th September 1991 (Follett, 1996)].

BEHAVIOUR AND LIFE CYCLE Adults fly rapidly, typically patrolling a territory, within a metre of the water surface and usually in the dappled or relatively deep shade of overhanging trees. More occasionally they will fly in the open, when the flight is typically slower and may include moments of hovering. Where it occurs with Downy Emerald, each species tends to occupy a different air space with male Brilliant Emeralds typically flying higher.

Females may fly high along forest rides or wood margins and both sexes may fly well into the evening on warm summer days. Woodland rides and margins are important for dispersal and movement between breeding sites, for the species is not reported from unwooded habitats such as open heathland.

Ovipositing females are not attended by the male. Oviposition is in wet bankside mud or detritus, always in the shade where branches hang low over the water, or amongst Sallow or Alder carr at the water's edge where tangled roots are exposed in shallow water. Larvae live amongst submerged detritus where the water is shaded, and take two years to develop. Emergence on the Basingstoke Canal has been reported on waterside grasses and Bramble shoots (D. and J. Dell, personal communication), but given the preferred site for oviposition (which typically is of difficult access to humans), emergence might also be expected at the water's edge.

The Brilliant and Downy Emeralds are similar in appearance, occupy similar habitats, share the same flight period during June and July and often occur together. The records used in compiling this account are taken on trust as correct, the reports coming from experienced observers, but it is possible that there has been some confusion between the two species.

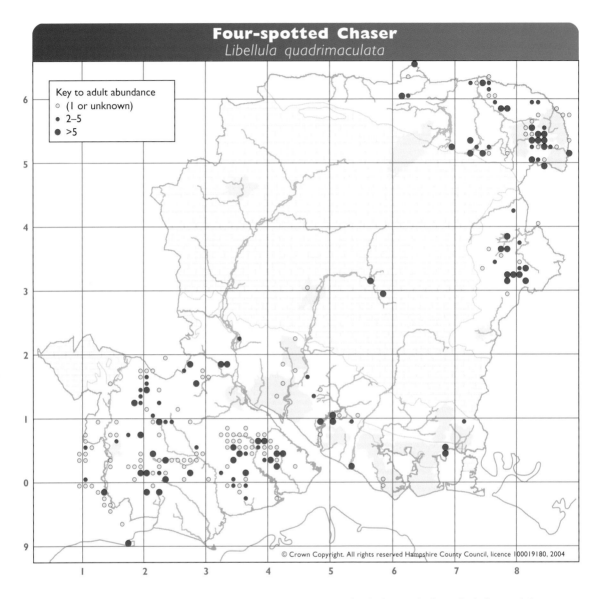

Four-spotted Chaser
Libellula quadrimaculata

Key to adult abundance
○ (1 or unknown)
• 2–5
● >5

DISTRIBUTION The above map shows that this species is confined almost wholly to the habitats of the Tertiary rocks of both southern and north-eastern Hampshire, with a smaller scattering on the Wealden rocks in the east. The New Forest and the heathland region of the north and east are clearly the headquarters of the species, with the bulk of the chalklands being almost devoid of records. It might therefore be said to have the classic pattern for a dragonfly in Hampshire.

HABITAT Away from the chalk, the Four-spotted Chaser is found at most of Hampshire's ponds, pools and stretches of canal and is tolerant of brackish waters. It is also an early coloniser of gravel pits and may even be found in quite small garden pools, including a few on the chalk. It is more usually associated with boggy pools and frequently rests in the vegetation surrounding such ponds, where it may be 'put up' by walkers going through heathland. It also frequents the most important coastal localities, such as the Needs Ore complex, Titchfield Haven and Old Bursledon Nature Haven.

The larvae are bottom dwellers, to be found amongst the finer detritus of the ponds.

MAJOR LOCALITIES As this species may be encountered at many sites within the New Forest and in the north of the county, it would be difficult to list all the localities that would fit into this category. Certainly, the waters named in the following sub-heading would qualify for inclusion in this category, but they would not be the only sites to which the word 'major' could be applied.

POPULATION STRENGTHS At the most favoured sites, numbers in excess of 20 individuals may be found patrolling the margins of ponds and canals. Such sites include Rowbarrow Pond in the New Forest, Sable Waters, Shortheath Pond, Warren Heath, Hundred Acre Piece, Eelmoor Marsh SSSI, Bourley Ponds and Swanwick Nature Reserve, whilst similar numbers can be found at some sites along the Blackwater Valley and various pools along the county boundary with both Surrey and Berkshire. Where numbers are high, the heavily marked form *paenubilia* can be found, a form that has dark patches on the wing tips.

On several occasions, swarms of around 30–40 dragonflies have been seen feeding at a height of about 30 metres on a hatch of small insects over Rowbarrow Pond and it is thought that they are mostly Four-spotted Chasers. The dragonflies were in turn being hunted by a pair of Hobbies and it is also thought that this species may be a major prey item for the Hobby as these falcons hunt over mires and heathlands in the New Forest.

In mainland Europe the species is known to periodically form large migratory swarms and it is possible that local populations in Hampshire may occasionally be augmented in late summer by these strong fliers.

Emerging from larval case © *Alan Hold*

FLIGHT PERIOD In Hampshire the species is on the wing from the beginning of May to the end of September, although in the north of the county it becomes scarce after mid-August.

EARLIEST/LATEST DATES The earliest date for this early summer species is 2nd May 1990 at Holbury Mill Pond with the latest being at Titchfield Haven National Nature Reserve on 28th September 1993.

ADDITIONAL NOTES The males are highly territorial and survey their territory from a vantage point either from the marginal vegetation or from a bare branch to which they often return. They are extremely aggressive towards other males and most species that enter their territory, with the possible exception of the Emperor.

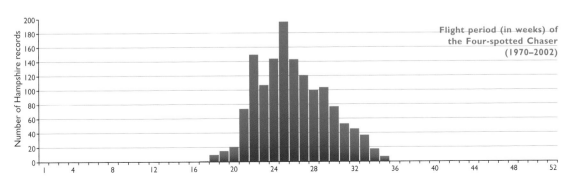

Flight period (in weeks) of the Four-spotted Chaser (1970–2002)

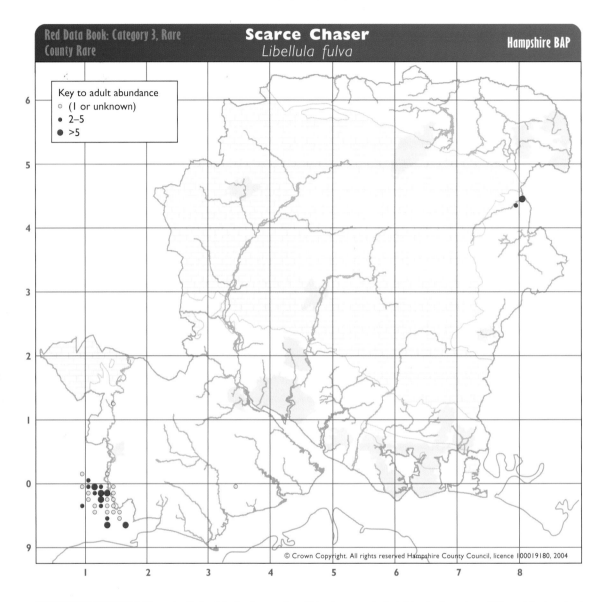

Red Data Book: Category 3, Rare
County Rare

Scarce Chaser
Libellula fulva

Hampshire BAP

Key to adult abundance
○ (1 or unknown)
● 2–5
● >5

DISTRIBUTION The only site for this riverine species within the present administrative boundary of Hampshire is a short section of the River Wey between Bentley and Farnham. The species was first recorded on the River Wey at Bentley on 23rd June 1996. Several adults were seen over subsequent weeks and it has been recorded each year since that date along this stretch of river and in surrounding meadows. Over 10 individuals have been seen at any one time, suggesting that a reasonable population is present in the area. Occasionally, individuals have been reported from nearby Alice Holt woodland (Don Tagg, pers. comm.).

However, since this volume covers vice-counties 11 and 12, there are several sites near Bournemouth where the species is still found along very short stretches of the Moors River, the River Avon and the River Stour. The celebrated site on the Moors River is the Troublefields Nature Reserve where the identification of exuvia and records of emergence have confirmed breeding. It is quite possible that breeding occurs at a number of other sites, as mature adults have been recorded at Merritown Heath, Trickle Cross and Fillybrook. Regular sightings have been made on the River Stour at Parley Green and East Parley Common, as well as Throop Mill and Blackwater. This species is frequently recorded in small numbers at Town Common, Christchurch, where newly emerged individuals have been noted early in the season. It is thought that this area is used for feeding and maturation of insects that have possibly emerged from the adjacent Moors River, Stour or Avon. In the Avon valley, records have been received from Coward's Marsh and Fairmile. Again, breeding may well occur along this stretch of the Avon, but confirmation is required.

HABITAT In vice-counties 11 and 12 the species is found on the two rivers named in the previous paragraph, one site being that of the small and slow-flowing Moors River where there is prolific emergent vegetation and the stream is overhung by trees on the western bank, and the other on the larger and more open River Stour on the outskirts of Bournemouth where there is also a great deal of emergent vegetation but little shade from bankside trees. The preferred habitat of the Scarce Chaser is unpolluted, nutrient-rich rivers with a slow to moderate flow, with patches of tall emergent vegetation such as Common Reed, Bulrush, Reed Sweet-grass, Branched Bur-reed and Yellow Iris. Areas that are heavily shaded by overhanging trees tend to be avoided. It is thought that this species prefers the sunnier areas that receive shelter not only from the tall emergent bank-side vegetation but also from nearby scrub. It is in these sheltered spots that the males may be found holding territory, but seldom much before late morning. More than one male, with little apparent aggression, may occupy one of these bays. The requirement for this specific habitat may well be the reason why this species is regarded as scarce to rare, though occasionally abundant, throughout its range.

The larvae are believed to develop amongst the silt and detritus that builds up around the roots of emergent plants where the flow is slack.

POPULATION STRENGTHS The populations along the Moors River in the late 1980s and the 1990s were regarded as being strong with regular counts of over 20

Male with mating marks on abdomen © *John Taverner*

individuals, but a visit in peak season and ideal weather conditions in mid-June 1996 produced a single-figured count. In 1991 it was described as "Still common in its favoured areas ....it maintains colonies on the slower reaches of the River Avon with quite good numbers in sheltered backwaters" (Winsland, 1994a).

FLIGHT PERIOD The Scarce Chaser is a spring species with its synchronised emergence usually occurring around the end of May but, depending on the season, this emergence may extend until the middle of June. The flying season is comparatively short, usually finishing by the end of July.

EARLIEST/LATEST DATES The Moors River provides both the earliest and latest dates, these being the 20th May 1990 and the 23rd July 1993 respectively.

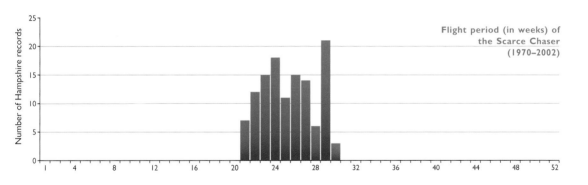

Flight period (in weeks) of the **Scarce Chaser** (1970–2002)

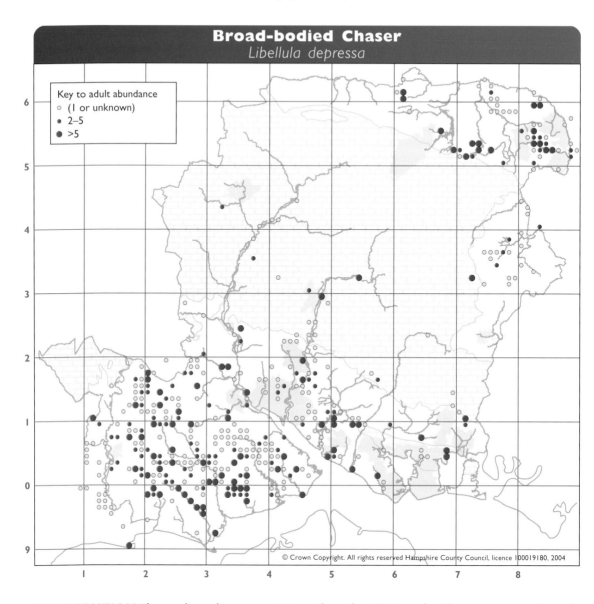

Broad-bodied Chaser
Libellula depressa

Key to adult abundance
○ (1 or unknown)
• 2–5
● >5

DISTRIBUTION The map shows a heavy concentration on the southern Tertiary rocks with some presence on other rocks to the south of the chalk, on the Tertiaries of north-east Hampshire and on the Wealden rocks in the east. There is also a very thin scatter on the chalk where records from a handful of garden ponds may suggest that such ponds on the chalk that are host to the species may be more widespread.

HABITAT The Broad-bodied Chaser is a species of ponds, pools, canals, ditches and gravel pits where there is still water and much emergent vegetation. It is an early coloniser of new water bodies such as gravel pits and garden ponds, an illustration of this coming from the top of Stockbridge Down where the National Trust created a dew-pond in the fashion of those that were once the main source of water on chalk downs. Within two years of the dew-pond being made, three male Broad-bodied Chasers were holding territories on the pond and females were visiting, mating and ovipositing. The larvae tend to ambush their prey, lying concealed in the fine detritus on the pond bed with just their head and the tip of the abdomen showing. Many of the shallow pools in the New Forest support breeding colonies of this species.

MAJOR LOCALITIES This is such a widespread species in suitable habitat, and there are so many sites in Hampshire where it occurs, that it would take a long list to name all the major localities. Following emergence, this species disperses away from the breeding site and will wander far and wide in search of new habitat so that it can appear almost anywhere.

POPULATION STRENGTHS Although this species may be encountered at so many of our ponds and canal localities, its numbers rarely reach double figures on any one occasion. The exceptions that have been recorded include Peaked Hill on the 15th June 1994 when over 20 were estimated to be in the area, and at Yateley Country Park on the 27th May 1990 and Deadman Bottom in the New Forest, when on both occasions up to 15 individuals were seen. During late May 2003, up to 15 adults were seen around the sheltered pond in Little Wooton Inclosure in the New Forest, and a series of seepage pools along the Latchmore Brook support a very healthy population. 20 were also seen at Eelmoor Marsh on 30th May 1998.

FLIGHT PERIOD This is one of the first species to emerge in Hampshire, the flight season starting at the beginning of May and extending into the third week of September, but in the north of Hampshire September records are exceptional. The Hampshire flight season is a week or so longer than that given in the *Atlas of the Dragonflies of Britain and Ireland*.

EARLIEST/LATEST DATES This early summer species was found on the 2nd May 1990 at Holbury Mill Pond, whilst the latest record is the 20th September 1991 at Hale Purlieu.

Female resting on hedge © *John Taverner*

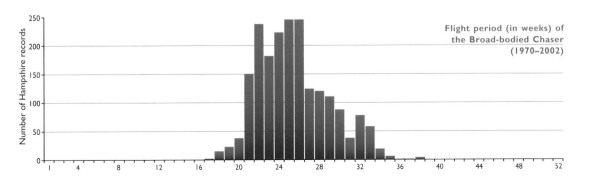

Flight period (in weeks) of
the Broad-bodied Chaser
(1970–2002)

Number of Hampshire records

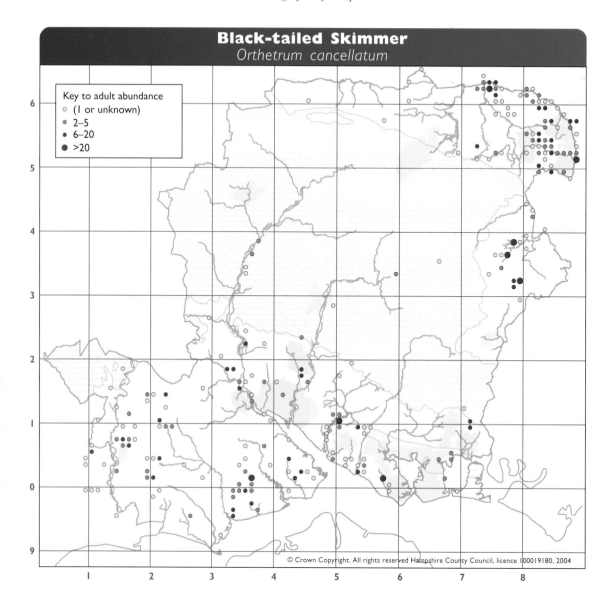

Black-tailed Skimmer
Orthetrum cancellatum

Key to adult abundance
○ (1 or unknown)
◔ 2–5
◕ 6–20
● >20

DISTRIBUTION This species has increased considerably in southern England during the last century and Hampshire has experienced its share of this expansion in range and numbers, taking advantage of such human creations as flooded gravel-pits and artificial ponds. The map shows a concentration on the Tertiary rocks of the north and south, but the species is by no means confined to these and can be found on all geological types in Hampshire.

HABITAT The Black-tailed Skimmer breeds in ponds, lakes, slow-flowing streams and rivers, dykes, old gravel-pits and a wide variety of localities where the water can be quite brackish. It is a pioneer species, often one of the first to colonise newly created water bodies such as newly flooded gravel-pits or newly cleared drainage ditches, often before emergent vegetation has been established. Its favoured sites often have an open aspect with areas of bare ground on which it settles to 'sun-bathe'; typical of this are the patches that fishermen use around their lakes that become bare of vegetation through frequent use.

MAJOR LOCALITIES The Black-tailed Skimmer is likely to be encountered at most large ponds and lakes and along the Basingstoke Canal. In the south of the county, such places include Hordle Lakes, Avon Valley Leisure Park, Broomy Pond, Eyeworth Pond, East End Gravel Pit, Swanwick Nature Reserve and Titchfield Haven Nature Reserve. Favoured spots in the central and northern Hampshire include Hook Common Pond, Alresford Pond, Bramshill Plantation, Eversley Gravel Pits, Shortheath Pond, Kingsley Pond, along the Basingstoke Canal at Farnborough and Aldershot and the River Blackwater. However, the species is so widespread in parts of the county that the above are simply a selection of major sites.

POPULATION STRENGTHS Males are very territorial and wish to command quite a large area, so it is not usual to find a large number of individuals around the edge of a pond or lake. Counts of over 20 would represent a strong population and examples of such counts have been at Swanwick Nature Reserve in June 1994, at Shortheath Pond in July 1994 and 1996, at Kingsley Pond in July 1994, and at various sites along the River Blackwater (Hants and Surrey) on a number of occasions. An exceptionally high count of 100 was made in the Bramshill Plantation complex in July 1993.

FLIGHT PERIOD This dragonfly is normally on the wing from mid-May until the end of August. However, in 1991 the first reported appearance was not until the beginning of July with the season extending well into the second week of September.

EARLIEST/LATEST DATES Our earliest record is 20th May 1990 in the New Forest at East End, whilst the latest is 25th September 1990 near Eversley in the Blackwater valley.

Adult female © *John Taverner*

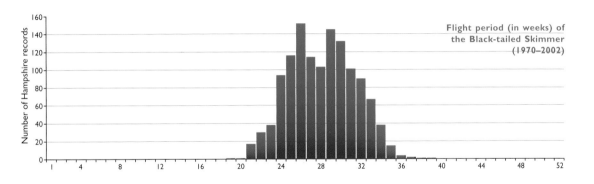

Number of Hampshire records

Flight period (in weeks) of
the Black-tailed Skimmer
(1970–2002)

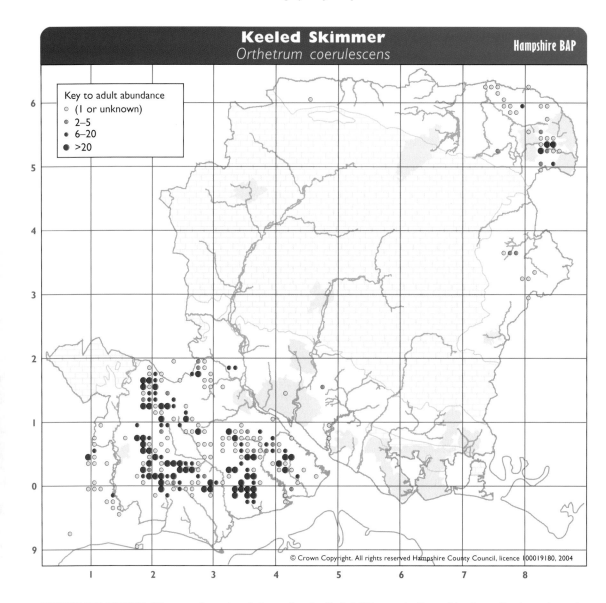

Keeled Skimmer
Orthetrum coerulescens

Hampshire BAP

Key to adult abundance
- ○ (1 or unknown)
- ◔ 2–5
- ● 6–20
- ⬤ >20

DISTRIBUTION Like several species of dragonfly, the Keeled Skimmer in Hampshire is confined mostly to the heathlands of the north and south with the New Forest being by far the most important area. Indeed, the New Forest would be important for this species on a national scale. During the six years of the national Key Sites Project (1988–1993), the species was recorded in 45 one-kilometre squares within the New Forest (Hold, 1995, unpublished) and was found at most of the Forest's mires and flushes. A small population is also found on the Wealden rocks.

HABITAT The Keeled Skimmer is a bog species, males patrolling the flushes, the boggy margins of rivulets and pools in valley mires that are set in areas of heath and moorland. The breeding sites are localities associated with *Sphagnum* mosses, Pondweeds and Marsh St John's-wort.

Adult male on Cross-leaved Heath © *Bob Gibbons* ➤

MAJOR LOCALITIES Many of the bogs, pools and seepages of the New Forest would qualify for the title of 'Major Locality' as the species is so common within much of the Forest perambulation. Typical New Forest sites include the Crockford Stream, Latchmore Bottom, Ober Water, Millersford Bottom, Rowbarrow, Burbush on the Burley Old Railway and Shatterford Bottom. Although not common in the north of Hampshire, it is recorded regularly from Shortheath Common, Warren Heath, Ancell's Farm Nature Reserve and at one or two sites around the Basingstoke Canal. At Eelmoor Marsh, it is one of the most frequently recorded species of Anisoptera, and is the fourth most frequently recorded odonate.

POPULATION STRENGTHS Many of the boggy areas of the valley mires in the New Forest hold large numbers of Keeled Skimmers. On sunny days at suitable sites, as many as a dozen males may be seen disputing territories with all dragonfly species along a 50 metre stretch of boggy runnel. It is not uncommon to find more than 20 individuals at suitable sites. In July 1989, July 1993 and again in July 1996, well over 100 individuals were recorded at Burbush on the Burley Old Railway. Similar counts were made in the Rowbarrow area in July 1990 and along Latchmore Bottom above Ogdens car-park and the surrounding heath on 12th July 1999.

Male developing blue pruinescence © *Peter Burford*

Numbers appear to be lower in favoured localities in the north of the county, counts of over 20 being made only at Eelmoor Marsh in every year since 1994, but 132 were recorded on 10th August 1997, 107 on 24th July 2001 and 175 on 4th August 2003. Also, 34 were at Crookham Bog on 14th July 2003 following management to create shallow scrapes.

FLIGHT PERIOD Whereas the *Atlas of the Dragonflies of Britain and Ireland* gives the flight period from early June to early September, records from Hampshire show that the Keeled Skimmer is often on the wing during the third week of May in the New Forest.

EARLIEST/LATEST DATES Our earliest date is 23rd May 1990 at Holbury Mill Pond, whilst our latest date is 1st October 1997 at Eelmoor Marsh.

BEHAVIOUR At a small bog seepage near Burley on 2nd August 1995, a pair 'in cop' were caught in a net. After they had separated in the net they were examined and released, whereupon both flew up vertically, only for the male to reform the tandem and attempt to mate again, demonstrating the intense urge of the males to mate.

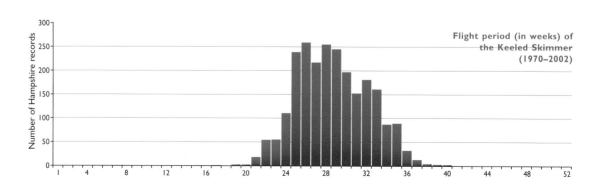

Flight period (in weeks) of the Keeled Skimmer (1970–2002)

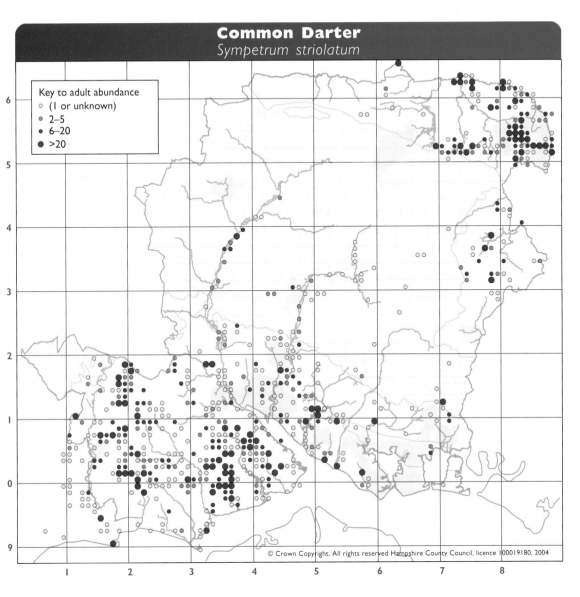

Common Darter
Sympetrum striolatum

Key to adult abundance
- ○ (1 or unknown)
- ● 2–5
- ● 6–20
- ● >20

DISTRIBUTION Amongst *Anisoptera*, there is no species so widely spread or numerous in the county as the Common Darter. The species is found in most corners of Hampshire in a wide variety of habitat types, appearing in well over 300 of the county's one-kilometre squares. It occurs on all the geological types, apparently as widely spread in the north as it is in the south, although the continuously suitable habitat in the New Forest makes the species especially numerous in that area.

HABITAT With such a widespread distribution, it is not surprising that the Common Darter is extremely catholic in its choice of habitat, favouring small garden pools, tiny ponds, large lakes, peaty bog pools, ditches, small streams, slow-flowing larger rivers and indeed almost anywhere that contains good quality water where it can breed. It is a pioneer species and will quickly colonise all types of water body, often being the first dragonfly to prospect a newly dug garden pond, even in the centre of towns. Individuals that have left water for whatever of various reasons may be found almost anywhere, from woodland rides well away from water to town gardens. One imagines that if the *Anisoptera* were to go into general decline, this would be one of the last survivors in Hampshire. The Common Darter is tolerant of low levels of pollution and slightly brackish water and will attempt to breed in

Pair in cop © *John Taverner*

situations that most other dragonflies will shun. It is not a demanding species and will breed successfully in waters with little or no emergent or floating vegetation.

MAJOR LOCALITIES With such a widespread species it is somewhat pointless to write of 'Major Localities' as there are so many waters, large and small, that would fit that description. As with so many dragonflies, breeding males are not tolerant of other males in their territory and this clearly restricts the number that a particular site can hold. However, where a population is particularly dense, this territorial behaviour can break down once pairs are ovipositing in tandem; for example, at Sable Pond on 27th August 2001, over a hundred pairs were engaged in oviposition, and at several points pairs were almost touching one another, jostling for position.

POPULATION STRENGTHS The previous paragraph gives an example of just one day's population of actively breeding adults that was in excess of 200 individuals. This was in an area that covered approximately two and a half hectares, consisting of one major pool with surrounding ditches and smaller pools set in a large expanse of heath and woodland. This would be considered a very strong population in Hampshire.

It is common to see well in excess of 20 adults patrolling, basking, mating or ovipositing in and around comparatively small water bodies. Counts in excess of 500 individuals have been made at various locations, including Hatchet Pond on 19th August 1993, Holbury Pond on 12th August 1990, Burley Old Railway Burbush on 20th July 1996, Rowbarrow Pond on 19th August 1990 and Wellington Country Park on 19th August 1996. On 23rd September 2000, a large assembly was seen on Hazleton Common, "flying like a swarm of mosquitoes with wings reflecting golden light" (John Vigay). Although some observations suggest a coordinated emergence, it is most likely a sign of a large population at those sites. Records from Hazleton Common, and in 2002 from the area around Blackwater at Needs Ore Point, were all of immature insects that must have been of similar age. The emergence period is spread out over the summer, with some emerging very late in the season. These individuals account for those that persist well into October and November.

FLIGHT PERIOD This late summer and autumn species is usually first seen on the wing at the beginning of July and the flight season will often extend to the beginning of November. During 2003 there were still a number on the wing in the first week of November, whilst at Needs Ore Point, on 16th November 2003, three pairs were seen in tandem with the females ovipositing in a shallow ditch. In the north of the county however, Chris Hall's experience is that this species *always* lasts into early/mid November and he does not regard records in the first half of November as in any way remarkable. His records for the second half of November probably occur in one year out of three and in early December 2001 there were several early December records at Eelmoor.

EARLIEST/LATEST DATES Our earliest record is the 30th May 1995 at Latchmore Bottom, whilst the latest is on 7th December 2001 at Eelmoor Marsh.

ADDITIONAL NOTES The species is a regular migrant to Britain, and Hampshire populations may be augmented by immigrations from the continent. In August 1996, Alan Hold found over 100 Common Darters feeding and resting along hedges bordering the salt-marsh at Needs Ore; an hour or so later, only a handful remained. This coincided with an influx of Painted Lady butterflies and Silver Y moths and these sightings were no doubt part of a mass immigration from the continent.

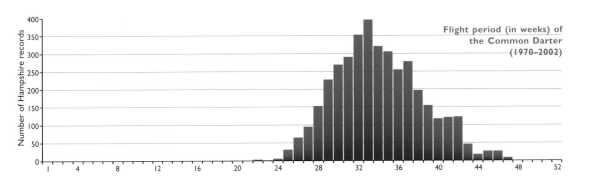

Flight period (in weeks) of the Common Darter (1970–2002)

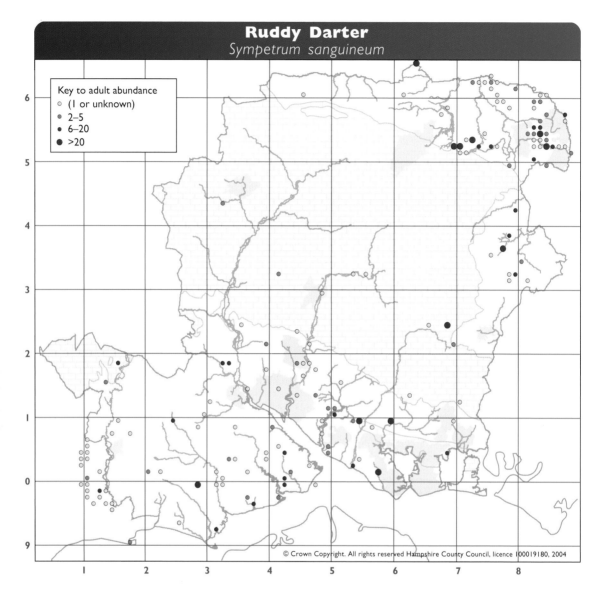

Ruddy Darter
Sympetrum sanguineum

Key to adult abundance
○ (1 or unknown)
● 2–5
● 6–20
● >20

DISTRIBUTION The Ruddy Darter has a very localised distribution in the county, although reports are coming from more and more localities. Whether this is due to better observer coverage or to a real expansion in the species' range is open to doubt, although there is evidence that the species' range in southern England is expanding. Where it does occur it can be reasonably numerous, although where it is found alongside the Common Darter, the latter is almost always found in far greater strength. However, on the Lymington-Keyhaven Nature Reserve, both species were described as "common", occurring in roughly the same numbers in 2003, whilst on the Avon Water Valley Reserve (SU307935), it was said to outnumber the Common Darter in 2003 by a ratio of 2:1. Up to the mid 1990s, the Ruddy Darter was not a common dragonfly in the south of Hampshire, with unconfirmed breeding records from Sheepwash Pond, Sowley Pond, Braemore Marsh, Burley Old Railway, Ladycross Pond, Holbury Mill Pond, Browndown and Hook Shore, with further sightings at Swanwick Nature Reserve, Titchfield Haven, Botley Wood and Farlington Marshes. It was more common in north-east Hampshire with breeding confirmed at Hundred Acre Piece, Hook Common Pond, Wellington Country Park, Bartley Heath, Lodge Inclosure and Yateley Country Park, whilst sightings at a few sites along the Basingstoke Canal suggest the possibility of breeding in that area; attempted breeding (oviposition) was recorded at Up Nately in 1993 and 1996 and on the Eelmoor to Claycart stretch in 1991 and 1992. Along the canal, Ash Embankment has produced fairly frequent records of adults. During the last decade, a number of other sites have been added to this list and at most sites the unconfirmed status no longer applies.

HABITAT The species occurs mainly in areas of acidic rocks, where a range of habitat is used, varying from small streams such as that at Crockford and very small pools such as Sheepwash in the New Forest, to large lakes such as Kingsley Pond and Shortheath Pond in north Hampshire. It favours sites with an abundance of vegetation both at the water's edge and along the banks, the latter being much used by males as lookout posts. At Sable Pond, Ruddy Darters are to found especially along one stretch of the lake where such conditions exist. It prefers to breed in the margins of waters, often amongst stands of Reedmace, Bur-reed and other emergent vegetation. It will select quite brackish waters in coastal ditches and pools where the emergent vegetation may well be Sea Club-rush. Open ponds and lakes, with limited vegetation on the banks, do not seem to be favoured. The Ruddy Darter will breed at shallow pools that dry out during the summer. Females can often be seen ovipositing over damp mud. Ova over-winter in diapause, hatching in the early spring, and the larvae then develop rapidly to emerge in June.

MAJOR LOCALITIES There are a few sites both in the New Forest and on the northern Tertiary rocks which hold populations that could place them into the 'major' category. In the New Forest, the tiny Sheepwash Pond is a locality where the species can be guaranteed in the right season, whilst Upper Crockford Stream is also an important site. The ponds in Exbury Gardens also hold a useful population. In the north of the county, Shortheath and Kingsley Ponds hold healthy populations. Otherwise, most sites mentioned hold good populations.

Adult male © Bob Gibbons

POPULATION STRENGTHS Sightings of over 20 individuals were noted at Bere Farm in the Wallington Valley in August 1988 and also at Browndown and Wildgrounds Nature Reserve in August 1990, whilst at Exbury Gardens, numbers on 14th July 2003 were certainly around 20 and only a part of the gardens was covered. Similar counts of over 20 in north Hampshire have been made at several sites along the Basingstoke Canal, including Claycart Flash in July 1991, Up Nately in August 1993 and August 1996, whilst away from the canal such numbers were seen at Bartley Heath in August 1989, Shortheath Pond in September 1990 and Hundred Acre Piece, Mortimer, in August 1991.

FLIGHT PERIOD The Ruddy Darter is usually on the wing from the end of June to the end of September, a flight period that is in line with that given in the *Atlas of the Dragonflies of Britain and Ireland*.

EARLIEST/LATEST DATES Our earliest record is on 18th June 1993 at Woolmer, whilst the latest is 3rd October 1993 at Wellington Country Park.

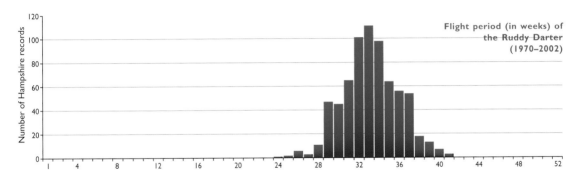

Flight period (in weeks) of the Ruddy Darter (1970–2002)

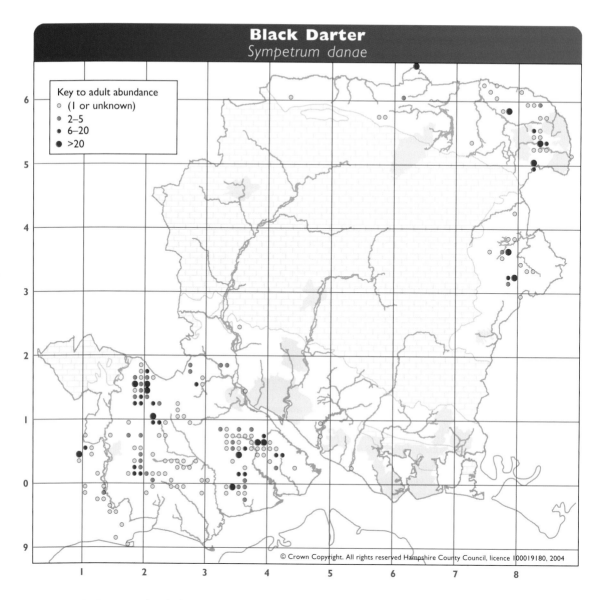

Black Darter
Sympetrum danae

Key to adult abundance
- ○ (1 or unknown)
- ● 2–5
- ● 6–20
- ● >20

DISTRIBUTION The Black Darter favours shallow, bog pool habitat. In Hampshire it is confined to the New Forest and a few remaining pockets of Tertiary rocks in the south of the county, along with a handful of localities in north and east Hampshire where areas of suitable habitat have survived urban development, road building and other such destruction of the heath that used to cover so much of the northern Tertiaries. The New Forest is by far the most important of these areas, with the species being widespread over much of the Forest heathland.

HABITAT The impervious nature of the New Forest rocks results in an abundance of small, shallow pools and ditches and these are the places to seek out the Black Darter. It prefers shallow bog pools with plentiful emergent vegetation, slow-flowing runnels and even seasonal pools where larvae may survive amongst damp mosses, but it is unlikely to be found on the larger and deeper Forest ponds. Adults may often be found well away from water, feeding over open areas of heathland or along plantation rides. As this is a migratory species, it may appear temporarily at water that is unsuitable for breeding. Suitable habitat in the heathland regions of north and east Hampshire is far more localised, but the Black Darter occurs at small heathland ponds that provide areas of shallow, well-vegetated margins and in the vicinity of bog pools. Prior to restoration, when the water was shallow, it could also be found along the Basingstoke Canal at Farnborough.

MAJOR LOCALITIES In its New Forest stronghold, typical sites are boggy seepages such as those at Latchmore Bottom, Broomy Pond, Furzey Pool, Stonyford Pond, Dibden Bottom, Rowbarrow Pond, Ashley Hole and the heath around Beaulieu Road Station. On the northern Hampshire Tertiaries, only a few scattered sites support good populations. These are Bourley Ponds, Bramshill Common, Cranmer Bottom Reservoir and Cranmer Pond, Eelmoor Marsh, Hundred Acre Piece at Mortimer and Shortheath Common.

POPULATION STRENGTHS It is not always easy to estimate the size of a local population, for individuals may be spread thinly over quite an extensive area. However, as this species is not very territorial, it is not uncommon to find several at a favoured breeding pool. At such pools, only a few metres across at Eelmoor Marsh, five, six or even eight may be encountered at a single visit (C. Hall, personal observation), though in the New Forest, where suitable habitat is extensive, the species is often reported at lower densities.

New Forest female at rest © *Cindy Allen*

In the New Forest, favoured breeding sites may have up to six males in an area of 500 square metres. Even in peak season it is rather uncommon to find more than 20 individuals at a site, although major localities will exceed this number in most seasons. Exceptional counts of over 100 were made at Dibden Bottom in July and August 1991 and again in August 1993.

In north Hampshire, numbers at Eelmoor Marsh have increased ten-fold from single-figure counts to 50+ following the creation of shallow pools and scrapes, the best count to date being 86 on 14th August 2002. At Bourley Ponds, near Aldershot, there was a count of 53 on 1st September 1996.

FLIGHT PERIOD The *Atlas of the Dragonflies of Britain and Ireland* regards this late summer species as being on the wing from mid-July to October, but records from Hampshire suggest that the county has an extended flight season compared to other parts of Britain. It is often seen at the end of June in the New Forest, but a week or so later in the north Hampshire. In the New Forest there are few records in October, but in the north of the county the species usually lasts at least until the middle of that month.

EARLIEST/LATEST DATES Our earliest record is on 18th June 2000 at Woolmer Pond, South, whilst our latest is on 27th October 1997 at Bourley Ponds.

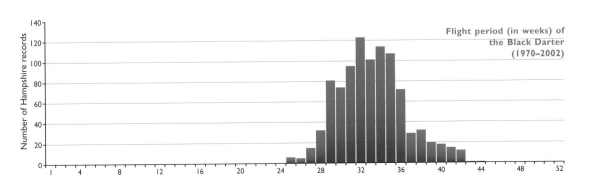

Flight period (in weeks) of the **Black Darter** (1970–2002)

Number of Hampshire records (y-axis, 0–140)

Vagrant Emperor
Hemianax ephippiger

Immature male © *Martin Goodey*

This strongly migratory species has been reported in Hampshire on four occasions, two of the specimens claimed as certain and the other two square bracketed. For Britain as a whole, records have become almost annual over the past two decades, though the total number seen has been very small and it is not known whether this increase in reports is due to a real rise in the number of arrivals or to the much greater coverage that dragonflies have received from field workers in recent years. The Hampshire records are as follows.

18th July 1984. A male was at Dibden and the following is an extract from the Journal of the British Dragonfly Society (Halstead, 1985). "On the 18th July 1984 a male *Hemianax ephippiger* was caught in the windscreen-wiper blade of my neighbour's car at Dibden, on the eastern boundary of the New Forest, Hampshire. It was shown to me within an hour of this happening when the insect was still alive but dying due to a split thorax. The brilliant blue of the first segment of the abdomen was outstanding but gradually faded over the next few days and finally disappeared". The insect was seen by Tony and Noelle Welstead, two of Hampshire's leading odonatists, who confirmed the identity.

2nd July 1990. A male was seen and photographed by John Horne at his dragonfly reserve at Old Bursledon. The photograph was small and not very clear, but it would seem to be a genuine record. This was also reported in the Journal of the British Dragonfly Society (Silsby, 1993).

[Late February 1998]. This was reported from Itchen Valley Country park and is described as *"Unidentified, but likely to be this species".*

[29th January 2002]. A dragonfly at Shipton Bellinger is also described as *"Unidentified, but likely to be this species".*

Red-veined Darter
Sympetrum fonscolumbei

Yellow-winged Darter
Sympetrum flaveolum

Adult male Yellow-winged Darter © *Peter Allen*

Noelle and Tony Welstead described these two as "rare migrant species" that "have been recorded spasmodically in the New Forest" (Welstead, 1984). In recent years, both species have been reported with much greater frequency in Britain, especially in southern England, and Hampshire has had its share of records. This must in part be due to the much greater interest in dragonflies today with a consequent increase in recorder coverage, but it is doubtless a real change that may well be connected with climatic change. We cannot guarantee that the following lists are complete, but recent records that we have are as follows.

Red-veined Darter – 2002 was clearly an outstanding year. 1 male, Old Bursledon Nature Reserve, 25th May 1997; 1 male, nr. Christchurch, 18th July 1997; 1 male, Old Bursledon Nature Reserve, 19th May 1998 ;1 male, Langstone area, 31st May 2002; 3–4, Lower Test Nature Reserve, 2nd June 2002; 1 male, Casbrook Common, nr. Romsey, 26th June 2002; 1 male, Burley, 18th July 2002; 1 male, Ibsley, 7th September 2002; 1 male, Hatchet Pond, 14th June 2003.

Yellow-winged Darter – August 1995 was clearly an outstanding time for the species. 1 male, Old Bursledon Nature Reserve, 2nd August 1995; 2 males, Old Bursledon Nature Reserve, 3rd August 1995; B category count, Itchen Valley, 6th August 1995; 1 female, Old Bursledon Nature Reserve, 9th August 1995; 4, Ancell's Farm, 12th August 1995; C category count, Mortimer West End, 12th August 1995; 2 females, Wootton pond, 13th August 1995; 40, Christchurch, 17th August 1995 (this count was made by Keith Goodyear, a most experienced odonatist); 18 at least, Itchen Valley Country Park, 20th August 1995; B category count, Warren heath, 21st August 1995; 2, Hengistbury Head, 24th August 1995; 3, Holmsley, 24th August 1995; D category count, Sopley Common, 26th August 1995; 1, Bramshill, 27th August 1995; 1, Woolmer, 1995 – date unknown; 1 female, Cove, 25th August 2003.

For this species, the list is probably far from complete, but it gives an indication of the species presence in Hampshire. As the species has successfully bred in the UK, any site in Hampshire where females have been seen ovipositing should be subjected to follow up visits later in the year and in the following year.

Scarlet Darter
Crocothemis erythraea

The unmistakeable adult male © *John Taverner*

Keith Goodyear, a very experienced odonatist, was lucky enough to see the fifth British specimen of this species on June 19th, 2002, at Upper Crockford in the New Forest. The following is from a letter that Keith wrote to report the sighting.

"At 16.45 hrs, a mature male *Crocothemis erythraea* appeared at a warm, shallow pool and flew several times over the pond before settling in adjacent Gorse where identification was confirmed using 8 × 30 Jenoptem binoculars. Observation continued until the specimen left, flying south. I have been familiar with this species since 1976 in the area around Les Saintes Maries in the Camargue where it occurs in large numbers, and was able to recognize the species by familiarity without recourse to literature. *Crocothemis*, in overall bodily proportions, resembles a small red *Libellula*, with its short flattened abdomen, rather than any of the *Sympetrums* with their long, narrow and more tubular abdomens, and the brilliant red colour of the males produces an unrivalled effect compared to any other European species."

"No other immigrants were seen in the area and the time of year would suggest a first generation specimen. The pool is largely ephemeral, containing very little vegetation or shelter, supporting only a small breeding population of Common Blue Damselflies. Its position is interesting however, in the context of previous British records. The first was from Cornwall in 1995; the second from the Isle of Wight in 1997; the third from Cornwall again in 1998 and the fourth was from Devon in 2000. All five have therefore been in the western half of England's south coastal counties."

"June 19th was a fine, cloudless day with 14.4 hours of recorded sun and a maximum temperature of 18°C with a 10 mph south-west wind. The previous day had 12.1 hours of sunshine, a maximum temperature of 21°C and a 5 mph wind. These two days followed a prolonged period of cool, wet and windy weather."

Keith's record has been officially accepted. The species is quite unmistakeable and an observer of Keith's knowledge and experience would have no difficulty in identifying a Scarlet Darter.

Small Red-eyed Damselfly
Erythromma viridulum

Isle of Wight male © *Peter Allen*

Possible newcomer

This species was first discovered in the United Kingdom during 1999 when three colonies were found in south-east Essex. In the following year, a number of sites were discovered on the Isle of Wight by Dave Dana. These discoveries were highly suggestive that the species was entering the country from various points along the coast and the number of sites on the Isle of Wight has increased with some sites supporting hundreds of individuals. The westerly expansion of the species' range has resulted in further discoveries in Surrey and Sussex and it is now likely that it will spread into Hampshire over the next few years, if it has not already done so. Searches have already been made at a number of suitable waters, but to date the species has not been found in the county. It favours ponds, lakes, reservoirs and ditches with abundant submerged vegetation. Water-milfoils, Rigid Hornwort and Canadian Pondweed are amongst the plants that particularly attract the species.

Lost species

Orange-spotted Emerald
Oxygastra curtisii

Adult male © *Bob Gibbons*

The Orange-spotted Emerald is extinct in the United Kingdom and has not been seen in the country since 1963. It was always a rare dragonfly, being recorded only from its Hampshire sites and at one in Devon at Braunton Burrows (Lucas, 1900). Lucas also mentions an unconfirmed sighting near Epping in 1871.

It was first discovered on 29th June 1820, by J.C. Dale at Parley Heath and described in *London's Magazine of Natural History,* Vol.7, p.60, 1834. This area was then part of Hampshire – now Dorset – and is largely covered by Bournemouth International Airport and housing estates. Subsequent records, all from the same area around Hurn (Hurne), Ramsdown and Pokesdown are sporadic. There was a forty year gap in records between 1834 and 1878, and Lucas reports no records between 1882 and 1900. Killington lists occasional sightings between 1901 and 1905, mostly from the Pokesdown site, and the species is then recorded intermittently until Keith Goodyear writes, in 1967: "As recently as 1949, as many as thirty specimens were seen in one day at Parley Heath".

In the *Field Guide to the Dragonflies and Damselflies of Great Britain and Ireland,* Steve Brooks states that he last saw the species on the Moors River in 1957 and at that time it was estimated that only about 4 km of river were suitable, and along the 1.2 km of that length that were inspected thoroughly, there appeared to be space for around six territorial males (Moore, N.W. 1991). Brooks goes on to say that the Orange-spotted Emerald almost certainly became extinct on the Moors River as a result of an accident that allowed sewage to enter the river upstream of the site, although the habitat along the Moors River had been much reduced by excessive shading of the river banks by overhanging trees (Moore, N.W. 1991). The effluent that did the damage was within permitted levels of quality set by the water authority (Gibbons, 1986). Pokesdown Heath, one of the classic localities, was ploughed up for public amenity purposes in 1966 (Goodyear, 1967), and urban sprawl has overtaken much of the rest of the areas used.

The last record for Britain was also from Hurn, when B.P. Moore captured a male on 19th July 1963, the specimen now being in the Natural History Museum in London.

PART FIVE

KEY SITES

The term Outstanding Assemblage Site (OAS) for Hampshire has been defined at the start of this book as one where 18 species breed or are likely to be found. A sample table of some of those sites is as follows, the data covering the years 1988 to the present day. The sites below have been selected because it is considered that few problems of access exist. However, sites marked with an asterisk require a permit and may charge an entrance fee.

Some Hampshire Outstanding Assemblage Sites

Site	Grid Ref	Site	Grid Ref
Ancell's Farm Nature Reserve	SU 8255	New Forest, Crockford/Peaked Hill	SZ 3599
Avon Forest Park, St Ives	SU 1203	New Forest, Crockford Stream	SZ 3499
Basingstoke Canal, Ash Embankment	SU 8851	New Forest, Long Pond South	SU 1901
Basingstoke Canal, Claycart Bridge	SU 8552	New Forest, Rowbarrow Pond	SU 3504
Basingstoke Canal, Eelmoor Flash	SU 8452	New Forest, Sheepwash Pond	SZ 3697
Basingstoke Canal, Norris/Pyestock	SU 8353	Old Bursledon Nature Haven *	SZ 4818
Basingstoke Canal area, Eelmoor Marsh	SU 8353 *	Parley Common, Ferndown	SZ 0999
Blackwater Valley	SU 8360–8062	Sable Waters, Embley Park *	SU 3318
Fleet Pond and Coldstream Marsh	SU 8255	Shortheath Pond, Oakhanger	SU 7736
	Probably no longer	Sopley Common, Hurn	SZ 1397
Holbury Mill Pond, Holbury	SU 4204	Swanwick Nature Reserve, Swanwick *	SU 5010
Hurn Forest, Moors River	SU 1000	Titchfield Haven NNR, Hill Head *	SU 5302
Merritown Heath, Moors River	SZ 1199	Town Common, Christchurch	SZ 1495
New Forest, Broomy Pond	SU 2110	Yateley Country Park, Yateley	SU 8359

The main aim of the Key Sites Project (KSP), that ran from 1988–1993, was to identify sites that have a large assemblage of dragonflies and also those places where nationally rare or threatened species were breeding or found regularly.

As Hampshire was recognised as having a large number of breeding species, an Outstanding Assemblage Site (OAS) for the county was regarded as one where more than 18 species regularly occurred. For counties having a less rich Odonata fauna a lower number of species constituted an OAS.

PART SIX

CONSERVATION INITIATIVES IN HAMPSHIRE

PROTECTING IMPORTANT SITES Many of Hampshire's dragonfly "hotspots" receive protection as Sites of Special Scientific Interest (SSSIs). Several have already been mentioned such as the New Forest, Basingstoke Canal, Rivers Test and Itchen, and Bramshill and Warren Heath Ponds. The management of such sites for their nature conservation interest has been less than perfect in the past due to the weaknesses of the Wildlife and Countryside Act (1981) which allowed the 'do nothing' approach or even benignly allowed competing pressures such as recreation to take precedence over the need to maintain wildlife interests.

The Countryside and Rights of Way Act 2000 strengthened the requirement for land managers to undertake positive management of their SSSIs, to ensure that land would be brought into 'favourable condition' for the habitats and species for which it is designated. Current auditing of the condition of SSSIs by English Nature will set the baseline against which future improvements can be measured. In addition, the designation of several SSSIs as Sites of Special Areas of Conservation under the European Habitats Directive, namely the New Forest and the River Itchen, will ensure that the 'favourable conservation status' of the Southern Damselfly is actively pursued, and will hopefully improve conditions for such species as the Scarce Blue-tailed Damselfly.

Nevertheless, SSSIs and SACs only cover a percentage of the countryside (albeit a slightly larger than average percentage in Hampshire due to the New Forest) and cannot be relied upon to conserve all species of dragonfly indefinitely. There needs to be a pool of sites suitable for supporting a diversity of dragonfly species throughout the wider countryside. There are several initiatives taking place to ensure this is happening.

SITES OF IMPORTANCE FOR NATURE CONSERVATION Whilst SSSIs are the best examples of certain habitat types and species populations at the national level, there are many more sites which are important at the county level. They are called Sites of Importance for Nature Conservation (SINCs) in Hampshire and receive protection from development through the local plan process. They are identified by the Hampshire Biodiversity Information Centre on behalf of Hampshire County Council, using criteria jointly agreed by the County Council, English Nature, the Hampshire Wildlife Trust and the District Councils.

Landowners are alerted to their presence and are encouraged to maintain and enhance their wildlife interest. Sites which have been designated as SINCs for their dragonfly interest include Embley Wood, Kingsley and Nutsey Ponds near Testwood and Dell Piece West, a shallow pond on open space in Horndean. Embley Wood has been mentioned earlier and, in fact, supports the minimum threshold of 18 breeding species needed to qualify as an Outstanding Assemblage under the SSSI guidelines. Included are several nationally rare/scarce species.

The agreed SINC criteria are mostly based on the presence of a certain habitat types, notable species (such as an RDB, Nationally Scarce, other legally protected species or county rare/scarce species), or important populations or outstanding assemblages. National or County status can only be attributed to a species once its distribution is known. This Atlas, the first for dragonflies in Hampshire, will enable the status of County Rare or Scarce to be attributed to various species. Sites regularly known to support breeding populations of these species will then be identified as SINCs. In addition, sites supporting outstanding assemblages of species will be identified as SINCs. Although no threshold has yet been formally agreed for an outstanding assemblage at the County level, a threshold of ten or more species is proposed on the basis that other counties which have a similar SSSI threshold of 17 species (i.e. and therefore have similar population distributions) have also set a threshold of ten.

In the definition of the SINC site boundaries, as with SSSIs, it is also important to include the semi-natural terrestrial habitats used for feeding and resting as well as the breeding sites themselves. Including the catchment may also be important in order to protect water quality and supply.

The Key Sites Register set up by the British Dragonfly Society is a valuable tool for focusing recording effort on the most important sites to ensure their interest is both monitored and maintained. The Hampshire Biodiversity Information Centre will use this Register to identify and protect all additional sites supporting notable species or outstanding assemblages. Landowners will be encouraged to seek help and advice to ensure that any management benefits the dragonfly populations.

THE HAMPSHIRE BIODIVERSITY ACTION PLAN The Hampshire Biodiversity Action Plan is a recent partnership-led initiative set up to identify and safeguard habitats and species of conservation concern in Hampshire. Detailed habitat and species action plans have been produced which identify specific actions that need to be undertaken and the lead agencies and partners for delivery of those actions.

A total of eight dragonfly species has been identified as being of conservation concern in Hampshire; Small Red Damselfly, Southern Damselfly, Scarce Blue-tailed Damselfly, White-legged Damselfly, Downy Emerald, Brilliant Emerald, Scarce Chaser and Keeled Skimmer. Although the Southern Damselfly is the only species to have been identified as a priority species in the UK Biodiversity Action Plan, the rest are considered important because they are either scarce or rare in Hampshire, or the county holds a significant proportion of the national population.

A detailed Species Action Plan has been written for the Southern Damselfly and many of the actions proposed in the Plan are currently being implemented by the Environment Agency and other partners within the Hampshire Southern Damselfly BAP Group, and described in the account of the species. Future action for the remaining seven species will be catered for by implementing the proposed actions in relevant habitat action plans for Open Standing Water, Heathland, Fen, Carr, Marsh and Swamp.

THE NEW FOREST LIFE 3 PROJECT This is a £3.9 million project run by a partnership consisting of English Nature, the Environment Agency, Forestry Commission, Hampshire County Council, National Trust and RSPB. The European Commission Life-Nature Fund awarded just over £1 million to the project. The overall objective is to restore the priority interest features of the New Forest cSAC and their supporting adjacent habitats in accordance with the cSAC Management Plan. In particular it is focusing on the restoration of the hydrology of the priority habitats and adjacent wetlands within the Forest and the re-establishment of links between fragmented habitats. As the Southern Damselfly is a priority interest feature of the New Forest cSAC, this can only be good news for dragonflies in general.

THE HAMPSHIRE HEATHLAND PROJECT The Hampshire Heathland Project is run by Hampshire County Council and sponsored by English Nature and the Heritage Lottery Fund under the "Tomorrow's Heathland Heritage" programme. The Project is working to restore 75% of the degenerate heathland outside of the New Forest, concentrating on heaths in the north and east of the county. Areas of wet heathland and acid grassland supporting shallow pools and ditches are being opened up and grazed for the first time in many years. The Foxlease and Ancell's Meadows SSSI is one such site benefiting from the work of the Hampshire Heathland Project; this site supports a population of Small Red Damslflies.

AGRI-ENVIRONMENT SCHEMES Besides the funds available from English Nature to support the management of SSSIs there are several 'agri-environment' grant aid packages available to farmers available from the Department of Environment, Food and Rural Affairs (DEFRA) that can be targeted at areas known to be of value for dragonflies in the wider countryside.

For example, the New Forest Heritage Area, River Valleys of the Itchen, Meon, Loddon, Rother and Wye, and Thames Basin Heaths are Target Areas for the Countryside Stewardship Scheme run by DEFRA. Key objectives include restoration of wetlands and creating buffers to protect watercourses and other wetland habitats from arable land or intensively managed grassland. Applications for Stewardship outside the Target Areas are also more likely to be successful if the land is recognised as a SINC or supports a species listed in the Hampshire and UK BAPs.

The new 'Entry Level' Scheme which is being piloted in North Hampshire by DEFRA provides a general package of financial support for a variety of wildlife friendly management options which all farmers can adopt – such as conservation headlands, over-wintered stubbles, hedgerow management etc. The guidance produced by English Nature and the RSPB specifically mentions the need to protect river and stream wildlife, such as fish and dragonflies, from soils and chemicals washing off the land. Management options include the use of buffer strips and changing the management of high erosion risk cultivated land. Improving the quality of our wetland habitats can only be good for dragonflies.

ENVIRONMENTAL IMPACT ASSESSMENT FOR USE OF UNCULTIVATED LAND OR SEMI-NATURAL AREAS FOR INTENSIVE AGRICULTURAL PURPOSES

Finally, new regulations came into force in February 2002 by Defra aimed at preventing "uncultivated land or semi-natural areas" being used for intensive agricultural purposes. The regulations define "projects" that require an Environmental Impact Assessment as those that *are likely to have significant effects on the environment.* In particular, the "in-filling of ditches, ponds, pools, marshes or historic earthwork features" for intensive agricultural use are defined as a `project' so that if a pond, ditch, marsh etc. supports a BAP priority habitat or rare species, then it is likely to have a significant environmental effect and the project should be refused. It is hoped that these regulations will lead to fewer ponds, ditches and other wetlands being lost in the wider countryside.

PART SEVEN

DRAGONFLY RECORDING IN HAMPSHIRE

Due to its wide range of habitats, particularly the New Forest, and its accessibility, Hampshire is a county which has been much visited and documented by naturalists over the past 240 years. Dragonflies, unfortunately, have not historically been as widely studied and identified as other orders such as birds, plants and Lepidoptera; for this reason there is not the wealth of early information on Odonata that exists for those groups. Gilbert White, in his *Natural History of Selborne*, first published in 1788, is disappointingly brief; in his "Naturalist's Calendar" section he gives April 30th and May 21st as earliest and latest dates for first appearance, between the years 1768 and 1788, of the "Dragon-fly (libellula)". Selborne, to be sure, is not in prime dragonfly country, but some more detailed observations by this great early naturalist would have made fascinating reading.

Baron de Selys Longchamps, the "father of Odonatology", published his *Revision of the British Libellulidae* (which covered all known British species of dragonflies and damselflies) in 1846. This was, principally, based on museum collections, and there is no evidence that he actually visited Hampshire. One of his correspondents was "Mr Dale of Dorsetshire", this being J.C. Dale who first described the Orange Spotted Emerald. This dragonfly was first discovered in the British Isles at Parley Heath on June 29th, 1820. Boundary changes in 1971 result in Parley Heath now being in Dorset (although still in vice-county 11, S. Hants). Other species mentioned specifically for Hampshire in Selys' revision are Golden-ringed Dragonfly, a very doubtful record of *Lestes virens* from the New Forest, and, from the same area, Small Red Damselfly.

In 1900, W.J. Lucas published his ground-breaking *British Dragonflies*. This drew together records for all known British species, and included detailed descriptions of appearance, habitat and distribution. It was the work on which much subsequent material was based.

F.J. Killington drew together further information in his *List of the Paraneuroptera (Odonata) of Hampshire and the Isle of Wight* (Killington 1926). Killington listed 34 species and suggested that two further species, Vagrant Darter and Scarce Emerald Damselfly, might have been overlooked; history proved him over-optimistic! However, he was correct in his assumption that the Ruddy Darter, which up to that time had only been recorded from the Isle of Wight, would be found on the mainland. He pointed out that there were considerable portions of the county that had been almost completely neglected by recorders (some things never change) and that the only districts in which the fauna were well known were Bournemouth (now considerably built over – and now in Dorset), the New Forest, Southampton and Eastleigh (both also now much changed) and Alton.

Killington's species accounts are interesting. He considered the Club-tailed Dragonfly rare (see Fraser), as he also did the Brown Hawker, especially in the southern half of the county; the proliferation of disused gravel workings have made the latter much more widespread. The Black-tailed Skimmer had very few records and he correctly assumed that it was probably overlooked, and he thought, similarly, that the Ruddy Darter, only recorded once, on the Isle of Wight, might be under-recorded, being mistaken for the much commoner Common Darter. No records of Scarce Blue-tailed Damselfly had been given "for some time", but he urged "paraneuropterists in the New Forest to keep a look out for it". History was soon to prove him right. He records the Red-eyed Damselfly as a very local species; it still is, although the aforementioned disused gravel workings have provided more localities.

Writing in 1903 in *Hampshire Days*, W.H. Hudson gave a short account of some dragonflies in the New Forest. The Emperor was "not uncommon there" there and the Golden-ringed Dragonfly was "a very common species in the southern part of the New Forest in July". The Beautiful Demoiselle was "one of the commonest dragonflies on the Boldre, the Dark Water and other slow and marshy streams in the southern part of the Forest" (Hudson 1925, Dent edition).

Cynthia Longfield's *The Dragonflies of the British Isles* was published in Warne's *Wayside and Woodland* series in 1937 and, as such, was the first widely available and affordable book on dragonflies. A list of vice-counties is given for each species, and 33 species are recorded as occurring in Hampshire.

A.W. Richards collected in the area of the Basingstoke Canal in the early years of the Second World War. He published his results in the Journal of the British Entomological Society for the years 1939, 1940 and 1941, and these provide a fascinating comparison with the fauna distribution today.

Lt.-Col. F.C. Fraser published *The Entomological Fauna of the New Forest* in May, 1950. Fraser collected in the Forest for over twenty years or more, often with Dr F. Haines, who lived in the area. He gives a clear description of the range of habitats and it is clear that these have generally changed little in the past half century; he is never a man to mince words, and is particularly deprecating about Hatchet Pond, the largest pond within the Forest. In relation to the status of species today, he makes a number of interesting observations. He describes the Small Red Damselfly as "perhaps the most common of New Forest Odonata"; there are places and times where that still rings true today, but it falls behind the Common Blue Damselfly and Azure Damselfly over all. He rediscovered the Scarce Blue-tailed Damselfly in 1930 after Lucas had described it as "disappeared, at any rate for the time being", and found it annually thereafter. He records the White-legged Damselfly as common throughout the Forest; this is certainly not the case today, when it is restricted to one locality. Similarly, he describes the Club-tailed Dragonfly as abundant, with its "true home" in the New Forest; he records seeing numbers in the hundreds, and collecting 25 specimens in 1935. *Aeshna mixta* has the vernacular name "Migrant Hawker", and Fraser says that he noted an annual immigration on the south coast between Barton-on-Sea and Swanage year after year during the second week in August. The Ruddy Darter, now regularly seen across the area, is still recorded as absent.

P.S. Corbet spent time in the county in the early 1950s when he was formulating his theories and writing his papers on "Spring" and "Summer" species of dragonfly. This was ground-breaking work by the man who has become the world's leading odonatologist of the last fifty years. In 1955, he published *The larval stages of Coenagrion mercuriale* using, incidentally, material provided by F.C Fraser. During 1952 and 1953 Corbet collected ova of the Large Red Damselfly from sites in the New Forest and Pamber Forest, and of the Beautiful Demoiselle in the New Forest and bred them through to emergence. The results were published in the paper *The life-histories of two spring species of dragonfly* in 1957.

K.G. Goodyear published *Observations on some of the scarcer Hampshire and Dorset Odonata* in 1967. In this, he still reports the exuviae of the now extinct Club-tailed Dragonfly as being "numerous" at its principal Hampshire locality (near Rhinefield in the New Forest). Keith Goodyear has published a number of papers on Hampshire Odonata and, in 1989, produced *The Dragonflies (Odonata) of Sowley Pond, New Forest, Hampshire*. This was the first exhaustive investigation of the largest still water body in the Forest, a lake that is strictly private, but holds the only population of Variable Damselfly. C.O. Hammond published *The dragonflies of Great Britain and Ireland* in 1983. This was the first complete, illustrated, user-friendly guide to the order anywhere in the world. He spent a considerable amount of time in Hampshire, collecting and illustrating specimens for the book, much of it in the company of Keith Goodyear.

In 1984 Noelle and Tony Welstead published their *Dragonflies of the New Forest*. This was the first of what was to become a widespread selection of local faunas, and was the result of considerable research by the authors, backed up by records of members of the New Forest Odonata Study Group. The book is illustrated with Tony Welstead's beautifully clear and accurate line drawings, all copied from his own photographs, and the text, as well as giving descriptions of twenty seven species occurring in the New Forest, succinctly describes their distribution, flight periods and life histories. The New Forest Odonata Study Group, consisting of some dozen or so amateur odonatologists, was formed in 1981, under the leadership of David Winsland, who remains at this time the leading authority on the dragonflies of the New Forest. In 1990 this study group, having dropped the word Odonata from its name, privately published a set of 1 km square distribution maps of all Odonata occurring within the New Forest, maps that were revised in 1992. Following the Key Sites Project, Alan Hold, in his capacity of Recorder for South-east England Odonata records, privately prepared in 1995 a *Report of the Odonata Recording Scheme Key Sites Project for South-east England* that covered the fifteen vice-counties that formed the South-east region.

The British Dragonfly Society was formed in 1983, and a number of local groups were formed under its wing. As well as the New Forest Group, which affiliated to BDS at an early stage, the 'Hants and Surrey Border Dragonfly Group' was formed in 1989 and has played an important role in the monitoring of dragonflies on the Basingstoke Canal. A monitoring scheme was set up and, in 1993, the results of five years' monitoring were published (Hall 1993). A second report, covering the years 1989–2000 was prepared on behalf os the Basingstoke Canal Suthority (Hall 2001). The monitoring scheme has since been discontinued.

APPENDIX ONE

LIST OF OBSERVERS

Both initials and first names have been used, according to how observers addressed themselves on record sheets.

Keith Alexander
Debbie Allan
Cindy Allen
Peter Allen
Neal Armour-chelu
J.G. Arnott
P.A. Arnott
Steve Bailey
R. Baker
A.M. Barker
M.V. Barker
G. Barker
P.J. Benstead
J. Birchall
Alison Bolton
Dr J. Bowers
J.K. Bowers
David Boyce
J.M. Boyd
S.J. Brakes
John Bratton
R.A.C. Brett
G.G. Brook
J.F. Brook
S.J. Brooks
Alan Budd
Phil Budd
Peter Burford
Richard Carpenter
Mark Cartwright
Clare Carvell
Steve Cham
Bob Chapman
Susan Clarke
E. Clement
John Cloyne
Christopher Cockburn
Simon Colenutt
Andy Collins
Barry Collins

J.R. Cox
R. Cox
J. Crook
Simon Curson
S. Davey
K.J. Day
David Dell
Jean Dell
Clare Dell
Graham Dennios
M & J Densley
Jonty Denton
D.E.J. Dicks
David Dimmock
Nick Donnithorne
T. Dove
Martin Drake
Barry Duffin
Pete Durnell
M. Edgington
Chris Emary
E.E. Emmett
V.E. Emmett
Chris Farris
J.E. Flory
R.N. Fry
Adam Fulton
Anne Galton
Neil Galton
Dennis Garatt
R.G. Gibbons
Joyce Gifford
Madge Goodall
Keith Goodyear
Andrew Grayson
David Green
S.J. Grove
Steve Guy
E.C.M. Haes
Chris Hall

Clifford Hall
K.H. Halstead
G.J. Harrison-Watts
Martin Harvey
Stephen Harvey
Roger Hawkins
Brian Hedley
Dorothy Herlihy
Peter Hodge
Alan Hold
Audrey Hold
Ann Holloway
Lawrence Holloway
T.J. Holzer
G.W. Hopkins
John Horne
David Hubble
Samantha Jacobs
J.F. Jeffs
Derek Jenkins
Terry Jennings
K. Johnson
Catherine Kemp
S. King
R.V. Lansdown
Mark Larter
Bob Leatham
Katie Long
Phil Lord
Keith Lovegrove
C.D. Lowmass
M. Lynes
M. Mayo
R. Merritt
Peter Miller
John Moon
Tony Mundell
Brian Nelson
C. Newbold
Tim Norriss

Tony Norriss
J.A. Norton
Matthew Oates
Chris Oliver
Jess Pain
Mrs M. Palmer
T. Pankhurst
Vic Pardy
H.D. Parkinson
K.R. Payne
C.L. Pepin
A.B. Petrie
N.J. Phillips
V.E. Phillips
Chris Piatkiewicz
Bryan Pinchin
Jane Plumridge
Keith Plumridge
Rod Pointer
John Poland
Dan Powell
Rosemary Powell
Rev E.A. Pratt
Col. E.D.V. Prendergast
Steve Price
B.D. Pummell
B.E. Pummell
Beth Purse
R.A.F. Odiham
    Group Conservation
W.T. Rankin
Gilbert Rowland
Ian Ryding
Michael Salmon
M. Scott
Rod Ship
A. Silcox
P.J. Simpson
A.C. Smallbone
Di Smith

G. Smith
Mary Smith
Matthew Smith
Southampton NHS
Mrs C. Steel
Tony Steele
J. Stenning
Alison Strange
Alan Stubbs
L. Summersby
Des Sussex

Brian Sutton
Graham Sutton
Jean Sutton
Tim Sykes
Don Tagg
Heather Tait
John Taverner
Mark Telfer
David Thelwell
Robert Thompson
Mike Thurner

J. Tubb
Elizabeth Tunnah
Graham Vick
John Vigay
Bill Wain
Chris Wain
A.M. Walker
M.C. Walker
Mike Wearing
D.J. Weaver
C. Webster

Andy Welch
Noelle Welstead
Tony Welstead
Robert West
Debbie Wicks
Gerry Wilding
David Winsland
P.A Young

SCIENTIFIC NAMES OF SPECIES OTHER THAN DRAGONFLIES USED IN THE TEXT

FLORA

Alder *Alnus glutinosa*

Bog Asphodel *Narthecium ossifragum*

Bog-myrtle *Myrica gale*

Bog Pondweed *Potomogeton polygonifolius*

Black Bog-rush *Schoenus nigricans*

Bracken *Pteridium aquilinum*

Bramble *Rubus fruticosus*

Branched Bur-reed *Sparganium erectum*

Broad-leaved Pondweed *Potamogeton natans*

Bulrush *Schoenoplectus lacustris*

Bur-reed species *Sparganium* spp.

Canadian Pondweed *Elodea canadensis*

Common Bent *Agrostis capillaris*

Common Cottongrass *Eriophorum angustifolium*

Common Reed *Phragmites australis*

Common Water-crowfoot *Ranunculus aquatilis*

Dog's Mercury *Mercurialis perennis*

Floating Sweet-grass *Glyceria fluitans*

Fool's Water-cress *Apium nodiflorum*

Gorse *Ulex europaeus*

Great Reedmace *Typha latifolia*

Hairy Sedge *Carex hirta*

Hard Rush *Juncus inflexus*

Hazel *Corylus avellana*

Jointed Rush *Juncus articulatus*

Lesser Pond-sedge *Carex acutiformis*

Lesser Spearwort *Ranunculus flammula* ssp. *flammula*

Lesser Water-parsnip *Berula erecta*

Marsh St John's-wort *Hypericum elodes*

New Zealand Pigmyweed *Crassula helmsii*

Oak *Quercus* spp.

Perennial Rye-grass *Lolium perenne*

Pondweeds *Potamogeton* spp.

Purple Moor-grass *Molinia caerulea*

Reed Canary-grass *Phalaris arundinacea*

Reedmace species *Typha* spp.

Reed Sweet-grass *Glyceria maxima*

Rigid Hornwort *Ceratophyllum demersum*

Rough Meadow-grass *Poa trivialis*

Rush species *Juncus* spp.

Sea Club-rush *Bulboschoenus maritimus*

Sedge species *Carex* spp.

Sharp-flowered Rush *Juncus acutiflorus*

Sphagnum mosses *Sphagnum* spp.

Thistles *Carduus* spp.

Tufted Hair-grass *Deschampsia cespitosa*

Water-cress *Rorippa nasturtium* agg.

Water-lilies *Nyphaea* spp., *Nuphar lutea* and *Nymphoides peltata*

Water milfoils *Myriophyllum* spp.

Water Mint *Mentha aquatica*

Yellow Iris *Iris pseudacorus*

Yorkshire Fog *Holcus lanatus*

LEPIDOPTERA

Painted Lady *Cynthia cardui*

Silver Y *Autographa gamma*

OTHER SPECIES

Atlantic Salmon *Salmo salar*

Bullhead *Cottus gobio*

Brook Lamprey *Lampetra planeri*

European Otter *Lutra lutra*

Hobby *Falco subbuteo*

Sea Lamprey *Petromy marinus*

White-clawed Crayfish *Austropotamobius pallipes*

BIBLIOGRAPHY AND REFERENCES

RECENT HAMPSHIRE WILDLIFE ATLASES

Eyre, J. and Clark, J. (1993). *Birds of Hampshire*. Hampshire Ornithological Society.

Oates, M.R., Taverner, J.H. and Green, D. (2000). *The Butterflies of Hampshire*. Pisces Publications.

Brewis, A, Bowman, P. and Rose, F. (1996). *The Flora of Hampshire*. Harley Books.

Goater, B. and Norriss, T. (2001). *The Moths of Hampshire and the Isle of Wight*. Pisces Publications.

REFERENCES

Bailey, S. (1997). *The Effects of Recently Created Water Bodies upon the Distribution, Habitat Use and Conservation of Odonata in the Blackwater Valley*. Thesis, University of Surrey.

Bailey, S. (2001). *Blackwater Valley Path*. Blackwater Valley Countryside Partnership.

Brooks, S and Lewington, R. (1997). *Field Guide to the Dragonflies and Damselflies of Great Britain and Ireland*. British Wildlife Publishing, Rotherwick.

Byfield, A. (1990). *The Basingstoke Canal – Britain's Richest Waterway under Threat*. British Wildlife 2: 13–21.

Cham, S. (1993). *Further Observations on Generation Time and Maturation of Ischnura pumilio with Note on the Use of Mark-recapture Programme*. Journal of the British Dragonfly Society 9 (2), 40–46.

Corbet, P.S. (1954). *Seasonal regulation in British Dragonflies*. Nature (London) 174: 655, 777.

Corbet, P.S. (1955). *The Life-histories of Two Spring Species of Dragonfly (Odonata: Zygoptera)*. Entomologist's Gazette 8, 79–89.

Crick, K and Bennett, J. (2003). *Blackwater Valley Dragonflies*. Blackwater Valley Countryside Partnership.

Defoe, D. (1724). *Tour through England and Wales*, reprinted in 1928 by Dent.

Eaton, J.W. (1994). *Basingstoke Canal Site of Special Scientific Interest Management Plan*. Prepared for Basingstoke Canal Authority, Mytchett.

Follett, P. (1996). *Dragonflies of Surrey*. Surrey Wildlife Trust, Pirbright.

Fox, A.D. (1987). *Ischnura pumilio (Charpentier) in Wales: a Preliminary Review*. Journal of the British Dragonfly Society 3: 32–36.

Fox, A.D. (1988). *Ishnura pumilio (Coenagriidae: Odonata) (Charpentier): a Wandering Optimist*. Entomological Record 101: 25–26.

Fraser, F.C. (1941). *The Nymph of Ischnura pumilio Charpentier (Order Odonata)*: Proc. of the Royal Entomological Society, London. A18: 50–56

Fraser, F.C. (1950). *The Entomological Fauna of the New Forest, 1. Order Odonata Fabr.*

Goodyear, K.G. (1967). *Observations on Some of the Scarcer Hampshire and Dorset Odonata*. Entomologist, January 1967, 16–19.

Goodyear, K.G. (1977). *Odonata of the Basingstoke Canal*. Unpublished report for Nature Conservancy Council.

Goodyear, K.G. (1989). *The Dragonflies (Odonata) of Sowley Pond, New Forest, Hampshire*. Journal of the British Dragonfly Society, 8, 8–14.

Hall, C.R. (1988). *A Survey of the Flora of the Basingstoke Canal*. Nature Conservancy Council, Peterborough.

Hall, C.R. (1993). *The Dragonfly Fauna of the Basingstoke Canal*. Unpublished.

Hall, C.R. (2001). *Dragonfly and Damselfly Records for the Basingstoke Canal 1989–2000*. Report prepared for Basingstoke Canal Authority.

Halstead, K.H. (1985). *Hemianax ephippiger (Burmeister) in Hampshire*. Journal of the British Dragonfly Society, Vol.1, No 5, 73.

Hine, A. (2000). *A Survey of the Macro-invertebrates of Eelmoor Marsh*. Unpublished report to Marwell Preservation Trust.

Hold, A.J. (1991). *Can Dragonflies Communicate?* New Forest Study Group Newsletter, 1, 3.

Hold, A.J. (1997). *A Survey of the Southern Damselfly (Coenagrion mercuriale) Undertaken at Itchen Valley Country Park, 1997*. Itchen Valley Country Park. NSSG (Bangor HQ).

Hudson, W.H. (1925 edition, originally published in 1903). *Hampshire Days*, Chapter 6, Dent.

Jenkins, D.K. (1991). *A Population Study of Coenagrion mercuriale (Charpentier) in the New Forest. Part 4, A Review of the Years 1985 to 1980*. Journal of the British Dragonfly Society, 7 1–4.

Jenkins, D.K. (1995). *A Population Study of Coenagrion mercuriale (Charpentier) in the New Forest. Part 6, Mark/recapture Programme*. Journal of the British Dragonfly Society, 11 1–4.

Jenkins, D.K. (1998). *A Population Study of Coenagrion mercuriale (Charpentier) in the New Forest. Part 7, Mark/recapture used to Determine the Extent of Local Movement.* Journal of the British Dragonfly Society, 14, 1–4.

Jenkins, D.K. (2001). *Population Studies on Coenagrion mercuriale (Charpentier) in the New Forest. Part 8 Short Range Dispersal.* Journal of the British Dragonfly Society, 17, 13–19.

Killington, F.J. (1926). *List of Paraneuroptera (Odonata) of Hampshire and the Isle of Wight.* Entomologist's Record Vol. XXXVIII.

Kingsley, R.G. (1918). *The Flora of Eversley and Bramshill Fifty Years Ago.* Proc. Of the Hampshire Field Club, 8, 129–138.

Longfield, C. (1937). *The Dragonflies of the British Isles.* Warne.

Longfield, C. (1949): *The Breeding Status of Aeshna mixta.* Journal of the Society of British Entomology 3: 84–86.

Lucas, W.J. (1900). *British Dragonflies.*

Merritt, R, Moore, N.W. and Eversham B.C. (1996). *Atlas of the Dragonflies of Britain and Ireland.* The Stationary Office.

Moore, N.W. (1991). *The Last of Oxygastra curtisii (Dale) in England.* Journal of the British Dragonfly Society, 7, 6–10.

Mundell, A.R.G. (1992). *Dragonflies of the Basingstoke Canal.* Unpublished paper for British Dragonfly Society.

Oates, M.R. (1986). *The Basingstoke Canal Entomological Report.* Unpublished report for Hampshire County Council.

Oates, M.R. (1990). *The Basingstoke Canal Dragonfly Fauna Between Fleet and Aldershot.* Unpublished report for Hampshire County Council.

Parkinson, A. (1993). *The Distribution, Ecology and Conservation of the Hairy Dragonfly within the Blackwater Valley.* M.Sc. thesis, University of London.

Parr, A. (2001). *Migrant Dragonflies in 2001.* Atropos No.15, 31.

Prendergast, E.D.V. (1991). *The Dragonflies of Dorset.* Dorset Natural History and Archaeological Society Proceedings.

Purse, Dr B. (2002). *The Ecology and Conservation of the Southern Damselfly (Coenagrion mercuriale – Charpentier) in Britain.* R & D Technical Report W1-021/TR, Environment Agency publication of work undertaken for PhD work by Bethan Purse under the guidance of the School of Biological Sciences at the University of Liverpool.

Richards, A.W. (1939). *Odonata in N.E.Hants and S.W.Surrey, 1939.* Journal of the Society for British Entomology 2, 61–63.

Savant, B. (1977). *The Status and Distribution of Dragonflies on the Tertiaries.* NCC files, Newbury.

Silsby, J. (1993). *A Review of Hemianax ephippiger, the Vagrant Emperor.* Journal of the British Dragonfly Society, Vol. 9, No. 2, 47–50.

Stebbings, R.E. (1993). *The Greywell Tunnel – An Internationally Important Haven for Bats.* English Nature, Newbury.

Strange, A. (1999). *Distribution of the Southern Damselfly on the River Itchen.* Ecological Planning and Research for English Nature and Environment Agency.

Tubbs, C.R. (1986). *The New Forest.* Collins "New Naturalist" series.

Tubbs, C.R. (1986a). *The New Forest.* p. 23. Collins "New Naturalist" series.

Tubbs, C.R. (1986b). *The New Forest.* p. 228. Collins "New Naturalist" series.

Tubbs, C.R. (1986c). *The New Forest.* p. 228. Collins "New Naturalist" series

Vine, P.A.L. (1968). *London's Lost Route to Basingstoke.* David and Charles, Newton Abbot.

Vine, P.A.L. (1994). *London's Lost Route to Basingstoke – The Story of the Basingstoke Canal.* Alan Sutton Publishing, Stroud.

Welstead, N. and T. (1984). *The Dragonflies of the New Forest.* New Forest Odonata Study Group for the Hampshire and Isle of Wight Naturalists' Trust. Eldertons Press, Southampton.

Winsland, D.C. (1985). *Preliminary Site and pH Evaluation for Assessing the Distribution of Coenagrion mercuriale (Charpentier) in the New Forest.* Journal of the British Dragonfly Society, 1 89–93.

BIBLIOGRAPHY

Dell, D. and J. (1996). *Odonata Data Summery 1990–1995.* (Unpublished).

Hall, C.R. (1993). *The Dragonfly Fauna of the Basingstoke Canal.*

Hall, C.R. (1997). *The Small Red Damselfly (Ceriagrion tenellum) in North East Hampshire.* Hants and Surrey Border Dragonfly Group Newsletter No. 22.

Hall, C.R. (2001). *Dragonfly and Damselfly Records for the Basingstoke Canal 1989–2000.* Unpublished report for the Basingstoke Canal Authority.

Hall, C.R. (1999–2004). *Eelmoor Marsh SSSI, Dragonfly Monitoring Reports for Each of the Years 1998, 1999, 2000, 2001, 2002 and 2003.* Annual Reports to Marwell Preservation Trust.

Hold, A.J. (1995). *Report of the Odonata Recording Scheme Key Sites Project for South East England.* Unpublished Report for Biological recording Centre.

Hold, A.J. (2000). *The Leckford Survey: A Report of the Odonata of the Leckford Estate.* The John Spedan Lewis Trust for the Advancement of the Natural Sciences.

Horne, J.M. (2003). *Old Bursledon Nature Haven. Dragonfly Report, June 2003.* Unpublished document prepared for this book.

Jacobs, S. (2002). *An Investigation into the Nocturnal Habits of Coenagrion mercuriale (Southern Damselfly).* Dissertation for a BSc in Wildlife Management.

Jenkins, D.K., Parr, M.J., Moore, N.W. and Silsby, J. (1996). *Environment Agency Species Management Guidelines, Southern Damselfly – Coenagrion mercuriale (Charpentier) 1840.* Environment Agency, 20–21.

Lucas, W.J. (1908–1909). *Notes on the British Dragonflies of the Dale Collection,* Entomologist's Monthly Magazine, 1908–1909.

Mayo, M.C.A. and Welstead, A.R. (1983). *Coenagrion mercuriale (Charpentier) on the Flood Plains of the River Itchen and River Test in Hampshire.* Journal of the British Dragonfly Society, 1.

Purse, Dr B. (2002). *Conservation of the Southern Damselfly in Britain.* Biodiversity Technical Series – Number 1. Report for the Environment Agency.

Richards, A.W. (1941a). *Odonata in N.E.Hants and N.W.Surrey, 1940.* Journal of the Society for British Entomology 2:117–119.

Richards, A.W. (1941b). *Odonata in N.E. Hants and N.W.Surrey.* Journal of the Society for British Entomology 9: 263–264.

Richards, A.W. (1941c). *Odonata in N.E. Hants and N.W.Surrey.* Journal of the Society for British Entomology 2: 61–63.

Stevens, J. and Thurner, M. (1999). *A 1998 Survey to Further Investigate the Status and Distribution of the Southern Damselfly (Coenagrion mercuriale) in Hampshire (New Forest, Test Valley and Itchen Valley).*

Strange, A. and Burt, S. (1994). *Southern Damselfly Coenagrion mercuriale: Survey at Itchen Valley Country Park.*

Strange, A. (2000). *Distribution of Southern Damselfly on the River Test.* Hampshire Wildlife Trust and Environment Agency.

Strange, A. (2002). *An Investigation of the Corridor through the New Forest for the presence of Southern Damselfly (Coenagrion mercuriale).* Environment Agency and Highways Agency.

Thompson, D.J. and Purse, B.V. (1999). *A Search for Long Distance Dispersal in Southern Damselfly, Coenagrion mercuriale (Charpentier).* Journal of the British Dragonfly Society, 15, 46–50.

Winsland, D.C. (1994). *Observations on the Current Status of Some of the Scarcer Odonata of the Vice County 11.* Journal of the British Dragonfly Society, 10 12–18.